W9-DCT-328

The Last Stitch

THE LAST STITCH

By

WILLIAM L. CROSTHWAIT, M.D.

and

ERNEST G. FISCHER

J. B. LIPPINCOTT COMPANY

PHILADELPHIA AND NEW YORK

Printed in the United States of America
Library of Congress Catalog Card Number 56-8189
First Edition

To the memory of my late wife

ROBERTA EUGENIA WISEMAN CROSTHWAIT

with love and appreciation

CONTENTS

The Last Stitch

PROLOGUE

ONE NIGHT in 1898 there was a great wedding feast in a Texas community. Tiger John Railton, a pioneer ranchman was a family man. He had reared a flock of boys and girls and the youngest of them had just married. The feast was spread, and the kith and kin from far and near arrived for the all-night frolic.

Everything went off fine, marred only by the whispering and winking of some of the oldsters.

"What d'ye know about that—Aunt Bess is showing," was the word that went around.

"Why, old Tiger John is too old, and Aunt Bess is nearly as old as Rachel of the Bible, and it's been twenty-one years since she's been that way."

There was general agreement that it was either a miracle or a scandal.

But for a whole year Aunt Bess went on showing and growing.

Then Tiger John sent for the family doctor. Old Doctor Jones—God bless his memory—sat by the bedside of Aunt Bess, and in his mild, kind and sympathetic manner, said, "Honey, you aren't pregnant; you have a tumor."

So the clan gathered again. This time it was not a festive occasion. There were few hospitals in Texas, and not one within a hundred miles of Tiger John's place. The nearest surgeon known to have operated on such a large tumor was hundreds of miles away. Finally someone thought of the young doctor who had just settled in the nearest town.

The young doctor had a kit of shiny new surgical instruments and, as the natives expressed it, "Sure as hell-fire, he's hell-bent on using them tools."

I'll admit I was proud of my certificate to practice medicine and surgery, fond of my operating instruments and ambitious to use them.

Eventually a committee was formed to meet with me to see what could be done about Aunt Bess' tumor. In the group were Dr. Jones, Tiger John and Tiger John's eldest son.

There was considerable reluctance to entrust Aunt Bess' loins to a knife in the hands of a stranger. But old Dr. Jones overcame objections by immediate members of the family. There was some grumbling among other relatives and neighbors, but the committee, after grilling me, decided to let me operate.

Dr. Jones assigned one of the older women of the neighborhood to assist. We went to work on Aunt Bess, stretched out on the kitchen table. Most of the rest of the community gathered under a big cottonwood tree in Tiger John's yard. There were several bad actors among them; might have been some of that old Texas moonshine, too, for all I know. One of these toughies, I noticed, had a lariat and was twirling it around rather playfully. Every once in a while he would lasso some cowpoke around the neck and jokingly throw the other end of the lariat over a cottonwood limb.

While I was watching this ruffian out of the corner of

my eye I heard him say, "If anything happens to Aunt Bess, Doc done took his last stitch." He didn't laugh when he said it, either.

It was hard for me to keep my mind on my work while all this was going on just outside the window, but we finally removed the tumor and sewed up Aunt Bess.

The tension eased somewhat when the old woman who had assisted at the operation went out on the porch and announced to the crowd, "Aunt Bess is going to be all right enough. Doc's 'bout got her sewed up again."

I was not so sure that Aunt Bess would be "all right enough," and I kept thinking about that deuced lariat and that cottonwood tree with limbs so slick they could be used for pulleys.

But after the operation I screwed up my courage and went out in the yard. The atmosphere out there was still pretty icy. However, old Tiger John sidled up to me and asked me what he owed me. I said $100.

Then he told me what I already suspected:

"I ain't got no money."

But Tiger John was an honest man:

"Tell you what I'll do. I'll sell my horse and pay you the money."

In those days when a man talked about selling his horse he was down to desperate business. When Tiger John talked about parting with his mount, I knew he wanted to pay.

I asked him how much he thought he could get for his horse.

He said, " 'Bout a hun'erd dollars."

I told him I needed a good horse and would like to see his.

Tiger John called one of his boys and said, "Go down there in the pasture and bring up Buck."

He brought Buck, by a halter.

I told Tiger John we might do a little swapping—I would take the horse for the price of the operation.

"But," I added, "I haven't got a rope to lead him with. If you'll throw in that lariat that fellow over there has got, I'll trade."

Tiger John walked over to the ruffian who had been playing hangman, took the lariat, tied it to Buck's halter, and handed me the rope.

I mounted my old horse and led Buck away. I was glad to have that lariat in my possession. And, in addition, Buck turned out to be a fine horse.

What about Aunt Bess?

She recovered all right enough.

On my way home I kept thinking of Aunt Bess, the surly mob and my lucky exit.

I anticipated that the period from my first stitch to my last stitch in my medical career would not be uneventful. I formed the habit of jotting down notes. Also I was blessed with a retentive memory. The story I am going to tell you is based on memory and memoranda.

As I write this, I am in my eighty-third year of life and in my fifty-sixth year of the practice of medicine and surgery. In my early career there were interludes as a teacher, a salesman, a printer and a reporter. These jobs were merely a means to an end, which was to become a competent surgeon.

EARLY TO RISE . . .

I WAS born on the second day of May, 1873, at six o'clock in the morning. Then and there I acquired the habit of waking up at precisely that hour. For more than eighty-two years I have varied very little from that habit.

The place of my advent was a split-log cabin situated in Chickasaw County, near Houston, Mississippi, U.S.A. I came from Cumberland Presbyterian and Primitive Baptist stock.

The family doctor, I am told, arrived a bit late, but in time to clip the umbilical cord.

He was Dr. Jacob Montgomery, who lived near Sparta, Mississippi, six miles from our cabin. He had to come horseback and follow a winding trail through a densely wooded area, and had to swim two overflowing creeks. The only people on whom my mother could depend in such events were a neighbor and my paternal grandmother, who lived nearby.

There were no obstetrical nurses; midwives were few and far between, and Grandma was in attendance until the doctor came. And she took charge when the doctor left.

My grandfather was awakened when my father shouted for my grandmother.

Grandpa decided he would celebrate. He was a squirrel hunter without peer, a real marksman. There was a fussy old wild turkey gobbler in the neighborhood. Grandfather took down his muzzle-loading rifle and slipped into the woods. He hid near where the wild turkeys came to do their courting. He blew a low note from a caller that he had fashioned from the wing bone of a wild turkey hen. Soon the big, bronze, red-snouted gobbler made his fatal mistake. He popped up in the open and lost his head with the crack of Grandpa's rifle.

They say Grandpa came in, proudly swinging the big bird over his shoulder, just as I made my appearance. They had a fine turkey dinner, country style. That is one turkey dinner I missed. Well, come to think of it, I didn't miss it entirely. Babies were put to the mother's breast as soon as they were born and scrubbed and oiled and dressed for the occasion. My mama had her share of the white meat and, of course, the liver. So, indirectly, I got mine.

Other things might have happened on which I never was briefed. I was told, though, that Grandpa was a great admirer of the Marquis de Lafayette, the French hero of the American Revolution, and he had named his second son Lafayette. So he insisted that I have that name, too. My mother wanted me to be named William Pinckney. They compromised by naming me William Lafayette Crosthwait.

"Crosthwait" originated at Derwentwater, a lake at Keswick, Cumberland, England, about three hundred miles northwest of London. The legend is that in 553 Christians came to the lake shore, made a clearing in the forest and planted a cross to mark a place of worship. They were called cross clearers, or crosthwaits or crosthwaites, the word "thwait" or "thwaite" meaning a clearer.

The Crosthwaite Church stands there today. Another landmark nearby is Greta Hall, where the poet Robert Southey lived, and he was buried in the Crosthwaite churchyard.

During the administration of President Ulysses S. Grant, military hero of the Civil War (or, the War Between the States, as most Mississippians prefer to call the fratricidal strife) the nation's financial difficulties became serious. Corruption and scandal in Washington shocked the nation. Hard money was the basis of our national credit, and paper money was inconvertible. The vanquished South was living under harsh reconstruction laws while carpetbaggers looted the public till.

During these times I was growing up as a barefoot boy. I wore pants, though. Most of the boys in our neighborhood, including the Negro boys and the sons of the hired hands, went in their shirttails until they started to school. The reason I wore pants was because my mother was a good seamstress and made all the children's clothing, including our go-to-meeting suits. One of the prettiest hats I ever saw was made by Mother and a neighboring young lady. It was made from bleached corn shucks (husks to you, maybe). The hat was of the sailor type. It created quite a sensation when my sister wore it to Sunday School.

My mother had ten children. I was the second. First she had three boys, one every two years. The last one died in infancy. Then she had three girls. The second girl died as a baby.

Jane Ardella was two years old when she became ill. She began to cough and strangle. Grandma said "get a doctor—she has a bad case of whooping cough." The only doctor available lived about two miles away. He came in staggering, took one look at the little blue-eyed darling and poured out a dose of laudanum, a preparation of opium.

I was big enough to observe what was going on. I remember my mother blowing breath into the mouth of the baby trying to inflate her lungs so she would continue breathing. But within two hours after that half-drunken quack had given her the dose of laudanum Jane Ardella was dead. We all grieved and for weeks my mother cried. I hated the very sight of that doctor and was truly glad when he fell into the hole in the creek and drowned.

Perhaps it was then that I got the idea that I wanted to be a doctor. Certainly it was obvious that we needed more and better doctors. But the very thought that a country boy, one of a poor family of many children, should aspire to be a doctor was frightening. At the same time I felt that I was predestined to achieve my ambition.

Three more boys came along after the girls. The youngest was weak. The old ladies of the neighborhood would come in and say, "Molly, you'll never raise him; he is the third, and you know the third one went before." We all worried about that third boy of that third lot. We humored and pampered him. He grew up to be the biggest and the most handsome of the whole brood.

Mother waited a few years and then had another girl. She was the last and is still living.

I grew up with a gang of playmates. White boys taught me to wrestle and fight. Colored boys showed me how to swim and dive and run and climb trees. Indian boys gave me the fine art of hunting with slingshot, blowgun, and bow and arrow. At an early age I became an expert with the blowgun. I could knock off a mouse, or lizard, or scorpion and sometimes a bird, at twenty to thirty feet.

The bow and arrow was quite a weapon in the hands of the older Indians and some of the white fellows, but not so effective in the hands of small fry. The slingshot was for distance rather than accuracy. All the kids had pea shooters and some were quite accurate with them.

I suppose there was color consciousness, but I never had the feeling that anyone was segregated. I know that when we raced for the old swimming hole and peeled off our clothes on the bank while someone shouted, "Last one in is a rotten egg!" it didn't make much difference whether your skin was white, yellow or black. The important thing was not to be a rotten egg.

One of our schoolboy sports was to place a small pebble in a pea shooter and shoot teacher in the seat when her back was turned. It was no use to try to pin the offense on any particular one for no one would dare tell even if he saw who did it. One day a man teacher, after being sniped two or three times, undertook to search the boys. The search was a failure because as soon as one boy was searched the others slipped him the pea shooter.

Where I grew up nearly all youngsters called their parents Pa and Ma. A very few of the so-called aristocratic caste called them Father and Mother; sometimes, behind their backs, they were "the old man" and "the old woman." We never heard "Dad" and "Pop" and "Mom" and "Mummy."

My parents were poor, but proud, honest, sincere, charitable, industrious and prudent. For thirty years, until the untimely death of my father, they lived that way. If they ever spoke a cross word to each other none of us children knew anything about it.

Pa was a Presbyterian; Ma was a Baptist. They alternated in attending each other's church.

Ma was the daughter of a Scotch-Irish Baptist preacher. He was a contemporary of the great evangelist, Lorenzo Dow. Dow, a Connecticut Yankee, was somewhat of a Billy Sunday or a Billy Graham of his day. For forty years he attracted crowds in the United States, Canada, England and Ireland.

I think my maternal grandfather must have caught the fervor of Dow. He served as pastor of churches in Alabama, where my mother was born, and in Mississippi, where she met my father and where they were married. During the summer Grandpa would range far and wide, holding camp meetings here and there.

By the way, these camp meetings were an institution. They were "protracted meetings." They were held in brush-covered tabernacles, usually in June or July. Some of the more distant residents would camp near the meeting place. There were sermons and songs in the morning and in the evening, and Sunday there was "preaching all day and dinner on the grounds."

Even as today, there were saintly hypocrites and honest sinners in the community.

One of our neighbors was a lazy drunkard. Someone referred to him as an "old bloat" and the name stuck. His wife had to run the farm and make a living for the family. They had one boy, named Henry. Henry worshiped his Pa, and he wanted to save him from drink. He contrived to get his father out to the meeting where the preachers and the deacons and some of the sisters—"the shouting gang," as we boys called them—teamed up to convert The Old Bloat.

After a fire-and-brimstone sermon, with plenty of

"Amens!" and "Hallelujahs!" thrown in, they sang, "When the Roll Is Called Up Yonder." I don't know whether that great song and the shouting made The Old Bloat forget John Barleycorn or not, but they got him up to the mourners' bench. After a while they got him down and were pounding him, and everyone was praying except those who were singing or shouting.

Little Henry, who was sitting 'way back, was getting excited, too.

Then The Old Bloat shouted, "I'm sanctified!" and fell into a trance. There was great rejoicing.

"Glory, glory! Hallelujah!" yelled one of the preachers to the other sinners. "Get aboard the grand old boat of Zion!"

That was too much for Henry. He lit out for home and breathlessly reported, "Ma, Pa is dead; they killed him at the meeting."

She looked up from her wood chopping and said, "How do you know?"

Henry explained that they had Pa down and beat him and then one fellow yelled, "Get a board—the damned Old Bloat is dying."

They used to lay out the dead on a board to cool off.

It was at this same camp meeting place that Johnny—one of my pals—and I attended night services. The preacher let go with one sure-enough hell-raising sermon. He drew a word picture of the lower regions so graphic and vivid that it left very little to the imagination. He scared the living daylights out of such sinners as us boys. My friend and I had gone swimming on Sundays, and we may have swiped a few apples and watermelons now and then. But there were some really wicked boys in the community; they had fished or hunted on Sunday.

While we were meditating our sins, the preacher kept piling up the brimstone, leavening it with rich pine knots and turpentine and stirring the fire until we heard the roar of the blaze and the shrieks of the damned. He pictured a grinning devil, forty feet high and equipped with a red-hot pitchfork, throwing the squirming sinners into that raging inferno.

Then they called up the mourners. Johnny and I sat there, trembling in our back-row seat. An old sister came and tried to pull us to the mourners' bench. We shrank back.

She said, "Ain't you boys afraid of the devil?"

I was too scared to talk, but Johnny, in a trembling voice, said, "Well, maybe I am afraid of that big, forty-foot devil the preacher talked about, but show me one my size and I won't be afraid of him."

We slipped out and ran all the way home. I had learned a useful lesson from what Johnny said that night, a lesson that has stayed with me to this day. During my time I've met a lot of devils bent on mischief. I have tried to whittle them down to my size. Then I was not afraid.

These camp meetings were not only religious revivals, but also social functions, political rallies and arbitration courts.

While every community had its meetin' ground, the larger centers were able to attract some of the better preaching talent. I remember when Sam Jones held a revival in Aberdeen, county seat of Monroe County.

Some of us wanted to hear that great preacher. We had no means of traveling to Aberdeen, about thirty-five miles away. But we got a lucky break. It was the custom for farmers to hold back a bale or so of cotton from the previous harvest to take to market in early summer. The proceeds from this bale were to replenish the larder until the new crop came in. It so happened that one of our neighbors was making such a trip just at the time when Sam Jones was in Aberdeen.

We—a deacon, another boy and I—went along and we stayed two days. We slept in the wagon yard, which, roughly speaking, was the motel of those days. In addition to listening to the preacher we explored the town. Some enterprising citizen had just set up an ice factory. No one had ever heard of such a thing where we lived. We were amazed at the fresh, cool, man-made ice as much as we were awed by Preacher Jones' hell-fire.

We dug down in our jeans, chipped in and bought a whole block of ice. The iceman packed it in sawdust in a big box. It looked like a coffin and we, like pallbearers, solemnly hoisted it into the wagon for the long trip to our backwoods community.

On the ride home we took turns sitting on that cool box. Our deacon got the longest turns. We figured he needed it because he got pretty hot at that revival meeting.

When we got home there was an all-day meeting going on. As soon as it broke up for dinner we unpacked our block of ice in the shade of the tabernacle. We told the folks we got it in the city and, what's more, that they were making it there every day—right slap-dab in the middle of summertime.

Some of the brethren and sisters whispered that we had gone to Aberdeen and backslid into the ways of liars.

But the deacon told them he saw, with his own eyes, how the city folks were making ice with a boiler and steam engine and a lot of pipes, and that they were making it out of ordinary river water from the Tombigbee.

We boys tried to back him up in his description of the details, but boys had very little standing in meeting-house trials in those days. The good brother and deacon stood before the congregation as a common liar, and they demanded a retraction and an apology. They had heard enough of the sins in the big cities without being told that hot steam could make cold ice from river water.

The upshot of the matter was that the deacon refused to back down and he offered to take a committee to Aberdeen to show them that what he spoke was the truth. They took him up on it, too, and the committeemen not only confirmed the report that there was a smoke-belching monster in the city making ice, but they brought back another block of ice. It was a great day in our community. The bitter issue was settled, and once again we were a harmonious community.

But it was a short-lived peace.

I have always believed in the efficacy of prayer. However, I think one should pray for spiritual things rather than material. Maybe we should have prayed then that peace would prevail, but we didn't. There were those who prayed for material things, and that started another rumpus.

It was a long, hot, dry summer.

One of our neighbors had a brickyard. He made bricks by mixing clay, sand and water, putting the mixture into brick molds, and placing the molds out in the drying yard where the sun would harden them somewhat. Then, for the final hardening process, the bricks were placed in a kiln, fired with wood. Along toward midsummer this fellow had a lot of bricks out there drying. He needed a few more days of hot sunshine before they were ready for the kiln.

Now, there was another neighbor who had a watermelon patch in the valley and the vines were just at the stage where they needed rain. The vines were drying up and the little melons were dropping off. The farmer just had to have rain.

Both the brickyard owner and the melon grower were prominent members of the same church.

The watermelon man promoted a called meeting of the congregation for the purpose of praying for rain. The brickyard man got wind of it and he made haste to go to the meeting.

The argument began.

The brickyard man contended that if the prayers were answered, the rain would ruin his bricks. The melon-grower said if it did not rain right away his family would starve because they were dependent on that melon crop.

The controversy raged furiously, and a good part of the congregation was drawn into one side or the other.

Meanwhile the clouds had been gathering in the south-east. Before folks ever got around to praying, the storm broke. It was the biggest rain and windstorm I had ever seen. A real gully-washer, you might say.

It washed away the melon vines and reduced the half-hardened bricks to clay and sand.

The two disputants had a fist fight before they got away from church.

I remember this episode because both fighters paid fines in my father's justice of the peace court, and I wrote up the minutes of the proceedings.

But it wasn't all trouble on a Mississippi farm in those

days. We had some fun, too.

Things were tough in Ireland, and a lot of Irish immigrants were coming over. My father employed itinerant ditchdiggers. We had one on the place when the possum-hunting season came in the fall.

A bunch of the boys got up a possum hunt one night, and Pat wanted to go along. He was a lot of fun, so we were glad to have him.

The dogs, though, got off the possum trail and ran a skunk into a hollow log.

As soon as we caught up we knew it was a skunk by the way the dogs were acting.

"Polecat!" one of the boys shouted.

Pat wanted to know what a polecat was. We explained that it was a kind of a cat and the reason it was called a polecat was because, once it was at bay, there was only one way to budge it and that was with a pole.

So Pat cut a sapling and rammed it into the hollow while we backed off.

But one spray and one whiff, and Pat ran back snorting, "Begorrah, let's stop up the 'ole and let 'im stink 'imself to death."

Pat was the gas-chamber executioner.

Then, although it was a crisp night, we took him to the swimming hole where he tried to wash off some of the scent.

But he had to sleep out in the harness shed for quite a while before he was allowed to come back in the house.

Pat always was a tippler, and one Saturday night he got really roaring drunk. Maybe it was because he was banished temporarily after the encounter with the skunk; perhaps that preyed on his mind. At any rate, he passed out, right behind the harness shed.

Some of the older boys decided to play a practical joke on Pat. When they found him out there dead drunk they carried him off to a nearby cemetery. There was a newly made grave there, where an old-timer who had died was to be buried the next day.

The boys gently lowered the inert form of Pat into the open grave. They went home, but returned early the next morning, hid behind nearby tombstones, and anticipated the pleasure of witnessing Pat's embarrassment.

About sunrise Pat roused himself. He stood up in the grave, saw the tombstones all around him, and shouted, "Glory, glory, hallelujah! It's judgment day and I'm the first son-of-a-gun to rise."

We had other sports, too.

There was log rolling, sometimes confused with birling. Birling was a sport that grew out of the lumbering industry; log rolling was a combined labor and sport of the farming country.

The latter cleared the virgin forest for cultivation.

It was the practice to clear out the brush and saplings and then chop a ring around the trunks of the larger trees so the sap could not rise. The trees would die and in a few years would fall or be blown down by storms.

In early spring the farmers would cut the fallen trees into ten- to fifteen-foot lengths. On a convenient day all the neighbors would come in for the log rolling, which was not really a rolling process, but a carrying or loading contest. Hand sticks or hand spikes were placed under the logs. Men took hold of these improvised handles. Often a real contest developed; each man would try to pull the other down, and a man felt disgraced if the shifted load forced him to his knees. Tricks were used to get a bulge on the start or to steal a few inches' advantage on the hand stick.

It was all in good humor, but I remember many strained backs, and I am sure many slipped discs and ruptures originated in these contests.

Come noon, the women would blow the dinner horn and there was a rush for the feast.

Usually the job was completed in the afternoon, the logs all piled in heaps ready for the torch.

Then came supper and a jug of eggnog. The local fiddler would tune up, and while the log rollers were getting their backs rubbed, the youngsters would take over with square dances, pigeon wings and backsteps.

These social gatherings, church services and the camp meetings were our main contacts with the outside world. Otherwise, our circle was limited to our nearest neighbors and our relatives.

I have mentioned my grandmother on my father's side. I liked to visit her.

Often she would be sitting in her rocking chair, looking out of her window and smoking her corncob pipe. Incidentally, she was an artist with a corncob pipe. She could rake out a small ember from the hearth and scoop it up with her bare fingers to light her pipe.

As she sat there, with contentment beaming from her wrinkled face, I would say, "Grandma, what are you thinking about?"

"Lawdy, child, I am thinking of things that happened 'way back yonder, things that made me happy. I know they can never happen again, yet it makes me happy to remember them now."

Then she made this observation:

"Son, always try to forget the evil or disagreeable things that happen to you and always try to remember the good or pleasant things."

That remark helped me to develop a philosophy of life that has enriched my existence.

She told me about the romance of my parents, too.

In their young days it was the custom of teen-age girls and older maidens, on the first day of May, to look into the water well and, from the shadows mirrored there, get a composite picture of their future husbands. From what she saw, my mother drew a picture of a tall, handsome young man with brown eyes and black hair, wearing a white shirt and collar, a black bow tie, checkered vest, dark britches, polished boots and silver spurs. She told her sister what she had seen with her own eyes and it must be so. A few Sundays following she was singing in the choir in her father's church when, lo and behold, her Romeo appeared in the congregation. They were married that fall.

It was Thanksgiving Day when he came riding in to his parents' home. Behind him, sidewise, sat his bride. Neighbors had gathered for a feast. They called it an infair dinner. That was a kind of offset to the wedding supper. The bride's parents gave the wedding supper and the bridegroom's parents provided the infair dinner, usually the day following the wedding night. Each tried to outdo or outfeed the other.

My father pre-empted the north forty of the quarter section of land which grandfather had bought immediately following the War Between the States. On the highest point he cleared off a spot, the neighbors gave a hand, and the split-log cabin and the leanto sprang into existence. That, with later additions, all painted white, housed the brood of eight and their parents.

My mother could do everything. She could get breakfast—ham, red gravy, hot biscuits, eggs, butter, syrup or jelly—faster than any short-order cook I ever saw. She could make a pound cake that would melt in your mouth. She could card wool or cotton, spin thread, weave cloth and make clothing for all the family. She could knit socks, stockings and sweaters. She was a spotless housekeeper, did all her laundry, tended her own flower garden and saw to the vegetable garden and the poultry yard. How she managed to find time to do all that I could never figure out. When I go into some of our modern homes and see things topsy-turvy, cigarette ashes and cocktail glasses scattered about and a sloppy cook in the kitchen, I wonder what in the heck has happened to our civilization.

Pa was a chip off the old block. He cleared up the forest and put the tillable land under the plow. He gradually expanded his holdings until he became what we called land-poor. Ma used to tease him by saying that all Pa wanted was the land that adjoined his.

Maybe the term "land-poor," seldom heard nowadays, needs explaining. It meant that a man had acquired so much land that the interest on his debts and the costs of maintenance and operation were so high that he was hard put for ready cash. Today a lot of us are gadget-poor; all kinds of labor-saving devices, but you work yourself to death trying to earn enough to keep up the payments and to keep the gadgets running.

So Pa was land-poor, but bighearted and public-spirited. He was school trustee and helped build the first frame schoolhouse in the community. He was road overseer and built the first all-weather road to the county seat, Houston, which was the railroad trading point. Roads were built and maintained by residents of the community. One of the obligations of citizenship was to contribute a fixed number of days of labor to the roads. Or you could pay the cash equivalent. But cash was scarce, and most men preferred to work it out. The overseer selected the work sites, supervised the jobs and saw to it that every adult male in the community contributed his just and equitable share to upkeep of the roads.

I guess Pa did all right on that job. They elected him justice of the peace. He set up a small country store and became the postmaster when a new post office was set up.

He kept a supply of commonly used drugs such as calomel, Dover's powder (containing ipecac and opium), quinine and phenacetin (aspirin had not yet appeared). I used to watch him dispense these remedies to the poor who had chills and fever, headache and biliousness, etc. Often he would say, "You ought to see a doctor."

But that was easier said than done. Many of the sufferers could not afford to buy medicine, much less pay a doctor.

Pa was a peaceful man. There were a lot of tough characters around and quite a bit of fighting and a few killings, but most everybody avoided trouble with Pa. There was a story that one bad actor did have a grudge against Pa and finally challenged him to a duel. Pa accepted with the proviso that he was to select the weapons. He stipulated broadaxes with the combatants' left hands bound together. The challenger called off the duel and later became friendly with Pa. Afterwards he shot one of his neighbors in the back and went to Texas.

We usually had long rainy spells in June. One day, while we boys and the hired hand were working on the woodpile, we spied a young deer playing among the cattle under a spreading sweet gum tree. Pa slipped in among the cattle and took his stand by the trunk of the tree. When the deer came by he grabbed it by a hind leg. Such a fight I have never seen again. The buck and Pa slipped and slithered all over the muddy ground. The deer kicked off Pa's shirt and ripped his britches, scratched him all over and drew blood in several places. Pa yelled for the hired hand to bring the axe, and Pa held on until the axe put an end to the fight. I asked Pa why he did not turn loose when the struggle got too hot.

He said, "Son, when you get ahold of something worth keeping, hold on to it."

We had nice juicy venison for several days thereafter.

From my grandfather I learned some lessons, too.

He was a Confederate veteran, an infantryman, who had been wounded in the fighting around Chickamauga, in northwestern Georgia. I used to spend one or two nights a week with him and he would talk for hours about the war. During the seesaw battle at Chickamauga he was wounded in both feet and found refuge in a hewn-log building called Brotherton House. People kidded him about having been wounded in both feet.

"You must have been running," they would say.

"No, it was this way," he would explain. "We had instructions from our officers that when things got hot and we were about out of ammunition we were to lie down with our feet toward the enemy. Otherwise I might have been shot in the head."

Anyway, talking to Grandpa I got briefed on the battles

of the War Between the States even before I was advanced enough to read about them in my history books. His son, my father, not quite fourteen at the time, took part as a home guard in the fighting around Corinth, Mississippi, and Shiloh, Tennessee.

To get back to Grandpa, after he got out of the Confederate Army he still kept his powder dry. I used to help him mold bullets to go squirrel hunting. There was a kind of dipper in which the lead was melted over a pine-knot fire. Then the molten lead was poured into a form to make a bullet. It was better to have a couple persons working at this. Once while Grandpa and I were doing this job he told me this story.

He said there were two very old men attending a funeral. In those days they called it "a burying." It was at the community cemetery. After the coffin was lowered into the grave, the clods shoveled in, and the dirt rounded and patted, the crowd drifted away. That is, all except two old-timers who aimlessly hung around the mound. Finally one of them approached the other and said, "Dan, how old are you?"

Dan said, "Well, I'm ninety-four."

His old friend said, "Well, Dan, there ain't much use for you to go home, is there?"

My grandpa was a wonderful man. Some of the most cherished memories of my boyhood cluster around association with him. On Saturday afternoons we went squirrel hunting. The timber grew tall and the wise old fox squirrels would go to the top of the trees to hide from the hunter. They always managed to get behind a limb. It was my job to go to the opposite side of the tree and shake a bush. The squirrel would shift his position. Then

Grandpa would say, "Hold, hold!" I would stand stock-still like a pointer and say, "Grandpa, shoot his eye out." Invariably Grandpa would say, "Which eye?" He rarely missed.

And he was a lover of good books, too. He always ordered leather-bound volumes. In his walnut bookcase he had Bibles, theological tracts from some English preachers, *Pilgrim's Progress,* histories of the Roman wars, Shakespeare and other great poets. He read and reread those books and, on rainy afternoons and at night, he often would read to me for hours at a time.

He was elected justice of the peace for our precinct. That was the same office Pa held later. The law seemed to run in our family. Grandpa bought some law books and was called "Judge," a title he did not like. He was fair in his judgments, but had a reputation for being hard on unfair fighters, habitual gamblers and hog thieves. It was all right to fight, but you had to fight according to the rules of the day, and an occasional wager was tolerated, too, but to get into the habit was bad. Hog stealing was a major offense any time.

A story often told might have been true; if you had known Grandpa you would believe it was true.

A farmer accused a generally well-known thief of stealing a hog. The defendant was brought into Grandpa's court. He had a lawyer from the county seat to defend him. They set up a pretty good alibi.

Nevertheless, Grandpa found him guilty and sentenced him to sixty days' hard labor on the public roads.

"But, Judge, we proved that man was out of the county when that hog was stolen," protested the defense attorney. "He could not have stolen it."

"Tut, tut," ruled Grandpa, "if he didn't steal that hog he stole some other."

And that was the law west of the Tombigbee.

The defense lawyer got a bit riled, but the courtroom audience applauded, and there was no appeal.

Grandpa was a hog raiser, too, and in order to be a hog raiser a man had to be a hog caller.

These days they have hog-calling contests, but they are commercialized events and the performances are indeed amateurish to anyone who ever heard Grandpa or any old-timer.

I regret there were no recording devices to preserve the old hog call for posterity. I can't reproduce Grandpa's call. On paper it might look something like this: Pig—pig—pig—Hoo-oo-ee! Hoo-oo-ee!

Our home was across the creek and valley ("the bottom," we called it) from where Granpa lived. We needed no alarm clock. Grandpa's hog call would awaken us. His hogs, too, knew his call. As his sonorous voice floated through the woodland, where domestic stock roamed at will, his hogs would come running and squealing to get their snouts in the feed trough first.

Grandpa was a successful farmer and tobacco grower, too. He processed his own tobacco and cured his own pork. He taught me the art and science of raising and curing tobacco. That included the planting of the seed, setting out the plants, and cultivating and worming the weed as it grew.

By worming I mean the removal of worms, which was a rather tedious process. No insecticides were available at that time, and each plant had to be inspected and cleansed by hand.

Grandpa raised tobacco for his own use and for his old cronies. At that time Grandpa's tobacco was widely known and his friends used to ride for miles to get a twist of it.

He'd keep his own chewing tobacco wrapped in a tanned doeskin to retain its moisture and its flavor.

Grandpa consumed large quantities of hog meat and chewed a lot of tobacco. Often Grandma would say, "Jimmie, if you don't quit chewing so much tobacco and eating so much meat, it will kill you."

It sure did, too. One morning when Grandpa was just past eighty-seven he ate a hearty meal of ham, red gravy and Grandma's hot biscuits. He took a chew of his favorite twist, and went out to feed his hogs.

He was stricken with a pain in his left chest and went to bed for the final rendezvous with his host of friends, comrades and relatives.

When he died, Grandma, known in the neighborhood as Aunt Jennie, took charge. She also lived to be about eighty-seven. Grandma was an Enochs and came to Mississippi from Tennessee. She had been reared somewhere around Nashville. She was personally acquainted with Sam Houston, who became President of the Republic of Texas, Andrew Jackson, who became the seventh President of the United States, and Davy Crockett, who died a hero's death in the fall of the Alamo.

We were distantly related somehow to Davy Crockett, but Grandma said he had been "a spoiled brat who just liked to hunt and fish." She was rather vague about our relationship.

When I was about ten years old a handsome, well-dressed man came to visit my grandparents. He was a Crockett and they called him cousin, but I don't recall his given name. The thing I do remember is that he wore a fine broadcloth Prince Albert suit, checkered vest and a massive gold watch chain and a large gold watch with "David Crockett" inscribed on it. I remember it because it was the first gold watch I had ever seen. The visitor said it was given Davy while he was in Congress.

Davy got fouled up politically, and he told his erstwhile supporters, "You folks go to hell—I'm going to Texas."

Now, to get back to Grandma.

To her last hour on earth she was a natural-born aristocrat. She smoked her pipe with finesse and dignity. She always kept a crock of brown sugar handy for us kids to swipe. She was a good cook and wonderful housekeeper. She hated bedbugs and gossiping women.

I am sorry for any boy or girl who is deprived of association with grandparents. Mine were among the people who made America.

But life back there was not always an idyllic existence in a sylvan setting.

About 1885 a local-option stock law was passed. That meant that livestock was not allowed to run at large. Rail splitting and fence building began. Hog calling became a lost art.

About 1886 the state of Mississippi went dry. A statewide prohibition law was passed.

(It is still, in 1956, one of two legally dry states of the union, Oklahoma being the other.)

Mississippi became the driest and, paradoxically, the wettest state in the union. Moonshiners and bootleggers flourished and the country became more or less demoralized.

Overgrown boys would come to school with a pint of

moonshine whisky in one hip pocket, and oftentimes, some kind of deadly weapon in the other. Some years we had only about three months school, but these boys did not take advantage of that. They rarely progressed beyond McGuffey's second reader and halfway through the old blueback speller. They dominated the noon-hour play period and made it doubly tough for us smaller boys.

One day one of these bullies shot an arrow at my brother. The arrow struck him in an eye. His eye was lost, and we despaired of his life. All kinds of messy poultices and irritating solutions were used. Infection developed, his face became swollen twice its normal size. The other eye became inflamed, and the prospect of total blindness became most evident. My mother finally dismissed the doctor and took over. She cleaned up Brother's face and began to use soft cloth packs wrung out in warm salt solution. He got well with the uninjured eye intact.

I pondered how long it would be before doctors knew more than mothers and grandmothers as to how to care for the ill and injured.

Another episode that spurred me on in my secret ambition to be a doctor occurred when one of my playmates and I spent a Saturday afternoon together that proved to be his last on this earth. We went swimming, picked some apples, ate a couple of them, and had a good time generally. The following day, about noon, his sister came to our house and told me that Jimmie wanted me, that he was extremely ill.

I went over to see him. His abdomen was swollen and he was vomiting dark fluids. His mother said he had become ill about eight p. m. Saturday. I recalled then that he had complained of a pain in his lower abdomen when we were playing together. Now he had a cramping pain in his upper abdomen and the pain settled in his right quadrant. They sent for the doctor. He came about midnight and told the family that the boy had a green-apple colic. The doctor gave him a large dose of calomel, placed on his tongue. He left a dose of laudanum and went on his way. I sat by Jimmie's bedside until he died that night.

I knew then that a fatal mistake had been made. We had eaten two apples, it was true, but they were ripe June apples, and, furthermore, Jimmie had taken only a bite of his apple and had given the remainder to me. He had eaten only a light dinner, and ate no supper. I felt then that there was need for doctors who knew more about what went on inside one's abdomen. Years later it dawned on me that my little friend had died of acute gangrenous appendicitis. Timely and adequate surgery might have saved him.

DESIRE TO DOCTOR

WHEN I told older boys that I wanted to be a doctor there were smiles. The idea of a gawky country lad becoming a real doctor was mirth-provoking.

Physically, I didn't show much promise either. I was anemic and malaria-ridden. I had had most of the diseases of childhood, plus undulant fever.

But my mother beamed with pride and joy when I told her I was going to be a doctor. She said, "You can make it."

My father was encouraging, but warned that I would have to earn my own way through school, and, then, "You'll starve to death." Doctors were overworked and miserably underpaid. Many of the hired hands and halvers (land renters under a fifty-fifty agreement with the landlord) were too poor to afford a doctor. Through the winter they lived on sowbelly and beans, and they had no money for medical services.

And there is an old German saying, "A doctor is an angel when you need him; a devil when you have to pay him."

But my decision to be a doctor became firm during a visit with relatives.

Summer, after the crops were laid by and the revival was over, was the time for visiting. One summer, when we had a new James & Graham wagon, my father hitched up his prize pair of mules and we all piled into the wagon and went visiting kinfolks in an adjoining county. After we had made the rounds of the nearer kin, on our way back home we spent the night in the home of a cousin of my father. This cousin was a Mrs. Murphree. Her son, Dennis, a babe in arms at that time, was to become lieutenant-governor of Mississippi for three terms, and twice he served as governor.

More important to me, though, was a young man I met there at the Thomas Murphree home. He was a Dr. Enochs, a distant relative. They called him "Buck." The place was a crossroads, forty miles from the nearest railroad, and Dr. Enochs was the only physician within a radius of twenty miles. Soon after our arrival there he came riding in on a magnificent bay horse. He greeted us with a hearty and friendly smile. He ordered the hired hand to hitch up his pony team; he had a call to make some distance away. I took this all in. And best of all, Dr. Enochs invited me to accompany him, which I did with alacrity. As the ponies jogged along toward home the doctor told me about the case and what he did for the patient. He recounted the joys and sorrows of a country doctor.

"If I had it to do over again," he said, "I might try to be a big-city doctor."

By the time we got home the stars were shining, the owls were hooting and the cry of the whippoorwill echoed through the piny woods. We sat down to a good supper, I became Dr. Enochs' roommate for the night.

The next morning I ventured to tell him that I would

like to be a doctor. He gave me an old *Gray's Anatomy,* which had been a standard text for some thirty years. Incidentally, *Gray's Anatomy,* several times revised and now grown to a volume of about 1,500 pages, is still standard. Dr. Enochs' copy showed much use, with a lot of penciled notes on the margins. He told me that anatomy was the most important thing to know. Pathology had not come into its own, and doctors knew little of physiology and chemistry. He had an articulated skeleton in the closet of his room. He also had an extra femur (leg bone) and he gave it to me. So the die was cast.

My brother, Robert Lee, was just twenty months older than me. He and I talked it over. We had always played together, sometimes fought with each other, and fought together when any older boy challenged either of us. How seriously we made our plans! We would take turns financing each other. I would study medicine; he would study law. He would teach three years while I went to medical school. Then I would practice medicine while he went to law school, and, in turn, he would practice law while I took a short course in law. The combination of law and medicine seemed logical. We planned to seek our fortunes in a large city, perhaps New York, Philadelphia or Chicago. Our imagination pictured office doors with our names emblazoned on shiny brass plates: ROBERT LEE CROSTHWAIT and WILLIAM LAFAYETTE CROSTHWAIT.

But, as I have said, times were hard, and it was a far cry to the city. Our farm was thirty miles from the railroad and cotton market at Okolona, Chickasaw County seat, in northeast Mississippi.

After the main cotton-picking season there usually was a scattered picking, or "top crop," late in the fall. The family doctor was supposed to get his pay from the top crop. But one fall, 1890, our doctor had been paid in cash plus a saddle horse.

Pa told brother Bob and me to pick a bale of cotton each from the top crop and to take it to market so we could buy our winter outfits. We worked hard for two weeks gathering the staple. Finally we had enough, about 3,200 pounds, to make two 500-pound bales of lint. So we loaded up to take our cotton to the gin and market. We made only about twenty miles the first day, so we camped by the side of the road, as was the custom those days. When we awakened the next morning we were covered by several inches of snow.

We arrived at the market, Okolona, about noon. We obtained a sample of our cotton, which we thought should grade at least fair to middling. We trudged from one store to another, and finally sold at four and a half cents a pound. The buyers claimed that our cotton was low middling.

We bought our winter outfits—suit, shoes and hat for each of us—and a few ribbons and toys for our younger sisters and brothers. Then we filled up on canned cove oysters and crackers, topped off with big red apples. We had a few dollars left. We slept that night in the wagon yard, and sunrise found us on our way back to the farm.

By that time I was sure that cotton farming was not for me.

When Pa made one of his infrequent trips to the market center he usually took one of us boys along. This three-day journey, there and back, was always a great event in the family, and I looked forward to my turn to accompany Pa on this great adventure into the world.

After I had read and reread *Gray's Anatomy* I felt that I needed more specimens of the human structure. I made my plans to procure more bones the next time it came my turn to go to market.

I had heard that railroads had hospitals at terminal points where they took care of their injured employes. When Pa and I arrived at the railroad town I took off for the depot to watch a train come in and depart. I figured the hospital must be around there somewhere, but I was acting casual and nonchalant, not asking any questions or anything. I found the hospital back of an old warehouse. It was a run-down frame building, poorly furnished with a few iron cots, and it was a rather smelly place. There was an old colored man who said he was the orderly, chief cook and bottle washer. I asked him if there were some human bones around about. He said, "No, suh."

That was a blow to my scheme. Surely, with all the railroad wrecks we were having at the time, there should be spare bones around a railway company hospital.

Curiosity overcame the timidity of a country lad, and I asked the old colored man what they did with all the arms and legs they cut off after railroad accidents.

He said, "Well, it's like dis: We generally keeps 'em an' buries 'em wid de patients."

It took me fifteen years to complete my skeleton. Then it took five years to get a medical degree and another ten years to make up for what I felt I had missed in medical college—but that is getting ahead of my story.

I had the ambition all right and the feeling that some day I was predestined to speak with authority on medical and surgical topics, but we didn't have the money for my education. I was a prisoner of environment and poverty, held captive by the necessity of finding employment within the sphere of our family influence.

I have mentioned the rural school I attended in the piny woods of east central Mississippi. King's Hill, it was called. It was two miles from our home via a footpath. Sometimes we had three months school during the year, sometimes as much as seven months. It all depended on how the tax money came into the school-district treasury and on how urgent the farm work was. Anyway, I got promoted from this one-room country school with highest honors. As I have indicated, the competition for scholastic honors was not too keen.

But highest honors gave me some standing in the community. Also at seventeen, I had just finished with the "seven-year itch" and ten years of malaria. And the teaching position at King's Hill school was vacant. As I recall it, the teacher, who had been boarding in the home of one of the school patrons, had got into an embarrassing predicament with one of the older girls in the family, and he had gone to Texas. So that fall, when no other applicant appeared, I applied for the teaching job and got it. The pay was $18 per month. Since I was living at home I could save money.

That was the first year of a total of five years of teaching, during which my pay advanced to $100 per month.

But even at $18 I earned enough to take a bookkeeping and commercial law course at Mississippi Normal College at Houston, Mississippi, during the summer.

My summers were mixtures of farm work, schooling, revivals, family visiting and business ventures.

One summer a newly patented bedspring was put on the market. I took a wagonload of those things and went peddling in east central Mississippi, down around Shuqualak, Noxapater and Wahalak. There were some Bogue Chittos and other remnants of Muskogi tribes in that area. Through the years they had settled down more or less. The bedspring manufacturer at Wahalak, a Yankee who didn't know much about Indians, had a hunch that they might like the comfort of this new spring.

So I was told to try my luck with them.

But the first thing I knew I ran into an Indian ball game. It was something like lacrosse. They used a stick about forty inches long, curved at the end. The bent end was cupped, and covered with buckskin thongs, something like a very crude tennis racquet. The hard ball, covered with tanned squirrel skin, was about the size of our regulation baseball. Under the rules of the game, the players were not allowed to touch the ball with their hands, but had to hit it with the improvised racquet. The object was to knock the ball over the opposing team's goal, like our football.

I hung around a while and watched the game, figuring that when it broke up I could sell some bedsprings. I was primed with a good sales talk in the pidgin English some of the Indians understood. I had some book larnin' in salesmanship, and the manufacturer assured me that he was giving me "virgin territory." Well, sir, this ball game went on for three days, with time out for eating and sleeping, and during that time no one would talk business. It turned out that this was the annual three-day festival when various tribes got together for a tournament. This one wound up in several fights, the Indians scattered, and I still had a wagonload of bedsprings. I can't think of anything more useless than surplus bedsprings.

The poor whites of the area were on the verge of starvation. The Negroes, after twenty-five years of emancipation, were not in much better shape. The ante-bellum mansions were crumbling in decay and the cotton aristocracy was going to pot.

The small cotton farmer and the small-town merchants were getting on their feet economically, and they were my best customers for bedsprings. I sold out, but not always for cash. Sometimes I took feathers, beeswax and other products in exchange. These items my employer could sell elsewhere for cash. Once I had to take a fiddle in trade, and we didn't know what to do with it. I finally traded it for a muzzle-loading shotgun.

In addition to the shotgun, a tidy sum of cash rewarded my summer's efforts.

My second year of teaching was at another one-room school called Prospect. You couldn't say there were grades in those schools. One hour you would be teaching the ABC's to a group of various ages; the next you might be trying to show some big, strapping fellow how to multiply. The "professor" boarded in the home of one of the school patrons.

The third year was about the same. As I recall it, the name of the school was Friendship. I boarded in the home of County Commissioner Jim Dandy, who had a big family and ran a cotton gin and grist mill. Dandy, a school trustee, had offered me the job. He said they hadn't been able to keep a teacher there because some of the bigger boys carried six-shooters and would run off the teacher. He offered me twice the salary I had been making, so I took it. For a few weeks things went well. Then the big boys, who had finished helping with the harvest, started to school. I could see trouble brewing.

One of those husky yokels taunted me: "Perfesser, what air yer rules? I don't see no rules on the board."

I said, "I have no rules."

When I rang the bell for lunch I told all the older boys to stay in. They looked at each other, and tried to size me up.

I said, "You fellows want an education or you wouldn't be here, would you?"

"Yep, guess so," they admitted.

"Now, I'm not making any rules. I understand you ran off teachers who made rules. I'm going to eat lunch. You write your own rules and then appoint a committee to see that your regulations are carried out."

One of those boys was pretty smart (he later went to the legislature), and he got my point. They drafted a set of rules. I was glad to see "No pistol-totin' " among them. They made and enforced other requirements, some of them more stringent than if I had made them myself.

This procedure, born of necessity, brought harmony to the Friendship school. The county superintendent, who was a kind of circuit rider among the schools, was pleased with the results of my experiment in self-government.

While I was trying to bring some degree of enlightenment to the backwoods I was not neglecting myself. I read everything I could get hold of—the weekly *Courier-Journal* from Louisville, the *Atlanta Constitution,* the *Memphis Appeal* and the local papers. Henry W. Grady's oration, "The New South," was a thriller for me and I memorized most of it. I borrowed a copy of the memoirs of Seargent S. Prentiss, and read all his speeches. Prentiss was a New Englander who moved to Natchez and Vicksburg, Mississippi, and gained fame in the South as lawyer. Among his masterpieces was his defense of a doctor who was tried on a charge of murder during a brawl in the old Gault House in Louisville. Since then I have heard several lawyers quote or paraphrase that speech in defending clients.

That was the day of the silver-tongued orator. The art of oratory, like the art of conversation, has suffered because we are becoming listeners (and lookers) rather than speakers. When great masses of humanity listen and look instead of speak their minds, it is an invitation to the demagogue.

The editorials of the great Henry Watterson of the *Courier-Journal* inspired me and many of my contemporaries.

I wrote short articles and sent them to the *Chickasaw Messenger,* published at Okolona. The editor invited me to come to see him, and when the Friendship school year ended, I lost no time in doing so.

The editor was Captain Frank Burkitt. He had three very bright children. His proposal was that I live in his home and tutor his children at night and work in the newspaper plant during the day.

My first job was setting type, by hand, of course. The Linotype had not been introduced there. I went through the usual initiation in a country newspaper shop. That consisted of looking for "type lice." After the type was used it was sprayed with water. Then the novice was told to search for type lice. While he was peering closely a printer suddenly would slam together several galleys of type. The inky water would splash into the novice's face, to the merriment of everyone except the butt of the joke.

I worked the adjoining type case to that of the head devil. This printer's devil was the outcussingest cuss I ever heard. He would fight at the drop of a hat, and drop the hat himself. He drank a quart of liquor every day. He was the editor's bodyguard and he carried a gun on his hip.

After I got to where I could set type fairly well, I learned to make up the page forms, to run off the papers on the press, and to fold them—by hand, too—ready to mail. Because I had been a schoolteacher and had reached the country rank of "professor" I was assigned to proofreading. That has helped me all through life. I can detect an error in copy or proof instantly; that is, all except my own errors.

The editor got the idea there had been some stealing going on down at the state capitol in Jackson. He wrote an editorial entitled "Wool Hats and Copperas Britches," which hinted rather strongly that some of the politicians in the capitol had been lining their jeans with public money. Captain Burkitt had been in the legislature and he wanted to run for governor. The state's financial distress gave him a ready-made issue.

When he got ready to campaign he sent me to Jackson to dig up some proof of his charges. I stopped at the old Edwards House. It was the first hotel of such size and luxury that I had ever seen. The old capitol was not far away. Both these structures have been replaced by fine buildings befitting the dignity of the home state of Jefferson Davis, L. Q. C. Lamar, James Z. George, Joseph Weldon Bailey, Thomas P. Gore and many others famed in the history of our country.

I began my work by frequenting the office of the

secretary of state, reading reports of the annual audits of state accounts. I noticed that certain items, supposedly bundles of cash, had been listed in the safe of the state treasurer, and counted as cash from year to year. I managed to get acquainted with the state treasurer and began to read his reports. I was posing as a law student.

One day some visitors from upstate came in. They wanted to see the safe where the state money was kept. The treasurer showed them everything and called particular attention to the several bundles which, he said, contained $360,000 in cash.

"That's for emergencies," he told the visitors.

At that time no one bothered to open the bundles.

Every department of the state government was in the red. Even as ignorant as I was, I suspected something was wrong and I looked with suspicion on the bundles of supposed currency. I reported to the captain. He again charged there was something amiss, some irregularity in the handling of state funds. He demanded an investigation by the legislature and an audit of the state's funds. The treasury was found to be $360,000 short. The bundles contained brown paper.

The treasurer was indicted, convicted and sent to the state penitentiary.

Despite this success, my editor was defeated in the election. I went back to Okolona.

One day soon after that, Captain Burkitt and I were alone in the office. His bodyguard-devil had gone home to lunch. One of the captain's political enemies had timed things just right. He was a member of the legislature who had taken offense at the editor's crusading. He came up just as the captain was stepping out of the office.

The visitor said something to Burkitt which I did not hear. The editor raised his cane to strike him. The legislator shot him with a large-caliber pistol. The bullet entered just outside the right eye and plowed along the skull, a half inch or less from the brain. The lawmaker ran. I called a doctor, who fixed up the editor.

It seemed to me that newspapering was a rather hazardous occupation, especially when mixed with politics.

Anyway, a much better-paying job was offered me as a teacher. That was October, 1893, and during that school year, closing in May, 1894, I was principal of the Burkett Institute. This institute, not far from our family home, had an academy rating equivalent to our high schools of today. They paid me $100 per month, a munificent salary. I lived at the home of a cousin who ran a general store. At night and on Saturdays I kept his books; in return he furnished my board and lodging.

Among my pupils at Burkett was Freddie Tickfaw. He was the meanest little devil I ever saw. After various other offenses he stole an agate marble from another boy. I reprimanded Freddie and made him return the marble. The next thing I knew Freddie pounced on the boy and beat him up. I had to give Freddie a good thrashing. I thought that closed the matter, but there was an aftermath several years later.

I was re-elected to teach at the same school another year, but I declined. I took a job in a mercantile establishment in Okolona. I had taken a business course during the summer at Mississippi Normal College at Houston, Mississippi.

The Okolona merchant operated a store where everything was sold—groceries, dry goods, hardware, sundries.

And over in one corner of the large store building he had a small bank. He also was a large planter. His store was a commissary catering to farmers all over the trade territory, covering a radius of about thirty miles. He promised me a job in the bank, come January 1.

As a country boy from a community where cash was scarce, the job in the bank appealed to me. I imagined a handsome salary went with the position. The prospect of financing uninterrupted education loomed.

Meanwhile the merchant put me to work in the grocery department. My job was to contact the farmers as they came into the wagon yard late in the evening and quote them the prices on such staple articles as coffee, sugar, flour, bacon and salt pork. In the early fall these commodities usually were purchased by the pound. After the harvest money came in, the farmers stocked up with larger lots.

The prices quoted had to be very low because there was great competition among the merchants. I was authorized to quote some very low prices. So, in the morning after they had sold their farm products and were ready to buy their supplies, a lot of the farmers came to see me at the store. I pictured myself as a pretty good salesman.

But I noticed that the head of the department kept monkeying with the scales on which the purchases were weighed. He would slip some kind of metal disc on the weights. I finally asked him, "What's the idea?" He said, "Well, we have to short-weight them or we would go broke, at our prices."

"Okolona" is a Chickasaw Indian word meaning "much bent." I would not say that this Okolona storekeeper was crooked, but he certainly was "much bent."

That night I told the boss I did not want to work where a practice like that was considered necessary. He put me in the dry goods department. We sold jeans, domestics, mosquito netting and calico by the yard. Then I discovered that the yardstick had been cut to about 33 inches. I raised a racket about that. They transferred me to the hardware department where there was neither weighing nor measuring. The first day a shipment of wagons came in. Me and another Negro, as we used to say when we thought we were hard done by, were told to assemble those knocked-down wagons, everything from the wheels on up to the springboard seat. Came Saturday night, my hands were blistered. I had a yen to do something else.

I went to talk to the fellow who was running the bank, the job that had been promised me. I found he was a cripple, had a wife and four children, and was working for $75 a month. He had no idea that he was slated to lose his job, and, after looking over the situation, I had no idea of taking it.

So I quit this merchant's employ. I had some money in my pocket by then and I decided to take a trip to Texas. The railroads were running thirty-day excursions. I had some relatives living in central Texas at a place called Holland, in Bell County. This town was destined to have a great deal to do with my career. It is a neat and law-abiding place today, but it was a shabby and rowdy hamlet back in the summer of 1894.

I got off the eleven p. m. southbound train. I was met at the station by a gang which proceeded to push me around and to "roll out the barrel," as they termed it. They called for the paddle and said, "Take your choice—treats or travel." They meant I could have my choice of treating the gang across the street in the saloon or I could get going.

The engine bell was ringing and the conductor was yelling, "All aboard!"

Maybe I should have taken the same train out that I came in on, but I didn't.

They draped me over the barrel and dusted off the seat of my pants with a few whacks from a paddle. I was rescued from further indignities by a friend of my uncle's, who happened by just as the gang was having sport with me.

Later I learned that all newcomers were given some sort of rough treatment the minute they got off the train. These Hollanders were a nuisance to trainmen; they would uncouple cars from a train, causing runaway cars to charge down the grade.

There is a story that when a conductor in Waco asked a passenger where he was going, the passenger said, "Going to hell."

The conductor said, "OK, I'll let you off in Holland."

The rowdies came to be known as the Stinkfinger Gang. They set themselves up as vigilantes. They played a prominent role in the early history of Holland and members of the gang were destined to cross my path in one way or another for years to come.

The custom of roughing up visitors seemed to be a sort of initiation into the life of the community. If you could take it they figured you could live there. I didn't seem to fit in too well.

After visiting with relatives and friends in town for a few days I decided to go out in the country where cotton pickers were in demand. The farmer boarded me and some more boys and paid us forty-five cents per hundred pounds for picking cotton. Working from "sun to sun," as they described a long day's work, I could pick about two hundred pounds. The oldest of the farmer's sons, who was twenty-two, could pick a thousand pounds a day. I worked just as hard as he did, maybe harder, but I didn't seem to make much headway. I was puzzled. The beautiful twenty-year-old daughter of the farmer took me in hand, watched every movement I made and coached me to the point where I increased my day's picking from two hundred to four hundred and fifty pounds. She taught me a trick which has served me well. That was to avoid lost motion, to make every movement count. Lost motion, false movement and indecision constitute a large part of the difference between the average and the master surgeon.

So I learned not only an elementary lesson in surgery, but I earned money to continue my education.

I chose National Normal University at Lebanon, Ohio. That was my preference because several members of the faculty of Mississippi Normal had graduated at National Normal and I had been impressed by my instructors' training. The Ohio institution was known as a rather progressive one for that day and time.

National Normal University counted among its alumni the late Cordell Hull, destined to become a great Secretary of State. He was remembered for his brilliance, especially in debate; for his quick wit, and for his undaunted courage and loyalty. Alfred Holbrook, a Connecticut Yankee who founded National Normal University, taught a class in ethics and logic, from five to six a. m., for three months in the winter. That course was compulsory. I was glad I had formed the habit of rising early. But as a farm boy with an humble start in life I felt it a privilege to be there, whatever the hour.

It was at Lebanon that I played my first football game, which also proved to be my last.

In those days the two great football mentors were Alonzo Stagg of the University of Chicago and Glen (Pop) Warner of the Carlisle, Pennsylvania, Indian Industrial School. Warner, who already had made a reputation at the University of Georgia, developed the Carlisle Indians into one of the great teams of the country.

Two of the students at National Normal—Fred and Harry Pierson, brothers—lived near Carlisle and were well acquainted with Pop Warner. I don't know just how they did it, but through neighborly friendship or somehow, they persuaded Warner to bring his Indians down to Lebanon to play the University. We thought we were pretty good. A victory over the Indians would put us on the map.

Now, at that time football was somewhat rougher than it is today. The flying wedge had been devised in the early '90s, at Harvard I believe, and this form of mayhem was all the rage about the time we met the Indians.

Like most rabid football fans, I still thrill to today's kickoff. In those days the kickoff was a fake. Usually the center just kissed the ball with his boot, tossed it back to a teammate, and the battle was on. The forward pass had not made its appearance, and the game was mostly foot-and-fist work. The playing field was 110 yards long, instead of today's 100, and there was no neutral zone at the line of scrimmage as we know it today. Under the rules, there was a sort of imaginary line through the center of the pigskin. An imaginary line always leads to trouble, whether in football or world politics. If a ball went out of bounds the man who recovered it brought it back to the spot where it went out of bounds and from there threw it back into play.

It was mostly line charging, not so much running around ends. If you got caught in the middle, with your teammates tugging you in one direction and your opponents pulling you the other way, you might find yourself drawn and quartered. In addition to great stamina, a football player had to have some ability as a wrestler, a boxer and a brawler. And sometimes the more articulate side won the arguments, thereby winning the game, so it was well to have a leather-lunged voice.

We thought we had all those requirements. Most players on our team were a rather beefy lot while the Indians were lean athletes.

The game was played on a Monday afternoon, in a meadow surrounded by rows of apple trees, with red apples of the "Johnny Appleseed" variety. At that time of year, in October, the trees were in full fruition. The ground was covered with ripe apples and we did not bother to clear them off the borders of the field. In the contest with the Indians we were run over, stomped, beaten and bruised; eyes were blackened, noses bashed in, arms and legs twisted, ankles sprained, a few teeth knocked out, and there were enough crushed apples on the ground to supply a cider mill. The play was fair and square, according to the rules of the day. We were defeated and deflated.

Incidentally, the score was 60–0. It wasn't even a good practice game for the Indians. None of the girls would brag on us, and few of our friends would sympathize with us.

That was my first and last game as a player, but I have

never ceased to have great zeal and enthusiasm for the sport, under improved playing rules, of course. I rate football and baseball as the two greatest competitive games in the world.

The apples on the football field remind me of a Sunday afternoon when a roommate and I set out to look for geological specimens on the Ohio countryside. Strangely enough, we found our way into an apple orchard. The trees were loaded and the ground covered with ripe, savory apples. Times were bad and apples were not selling very well. There was a drove of hogs eating the apples on the ground.

My companion and I, both with hearty appetites after a walk of several miles, picked up some choice apples which we proceeded to devour. We ate on the theory that if "an apple a day will keep the doctor away," we could store up some health insurance in that apple orchard.

While we were gorging ourselves, an old farmer came charging out on us and yelling, "Get out of here, you lazy bums, get out!"

When he stopped to catch his breath we explained that the ground was covered with apples, that his hogs were eating them, and we didn't think he would mind if we ate a few.

He said, "Well, I don't care how many you eat, but get them off them trees. Don't you know that a hog can't climb a tree?"

So we shinnied up a tree and ate our fill while the farmer's porkers went on about their business on the ground.

My studies at National Normal included one year of law and one year of pre-medical work as well as a course in civil engineering. A doctor should know something about the law and a lawyer should know something about medicine. What I learned there in both fields served me well years later when I became professor of medical jurisprudence at Baylor University.

After two years at National Normal they awarded me a degree of Bachelor of Science. By that time my funds were running low again.

But a few days before my graduation Professor Holbrook walked into the classroom, held up a telegram and asked, "Does anyone here want to go to Texas?"

There was no immediate response.

"I've got a telegram here," he went on, "from a school down there looking for a teacher and they pay a handsome salary. Crosthwait, you've been in Texas, haven't you?"

"Yes, sir, but I hadn't thought much about going back there. I need money to go to medical school, though. Professor, just where in Texas is this position?"

"Well, it's at a little place called Holland."

Stinkfinger!

I didn't tell the professor that I knew about the place. Nor did I mention my unpleasant experience with the Stinkfingers.

"Now, if you want the job," Dr. Holbrook added, "wire the man who signed this telegram. He is president of the board of trustees at Holland, and his name is W. S. Lanford."

Why, that's Uncle Sim, it struck me.

I had not kept up with my Holland relatives. I didn't know that Uncle Sim, a merchant there, was president of the board, and he didn't know where I was.

It was just another one of those coincidences that make

you ponder the possibility of predestination. I doubt that there is any person who cannot recall some incident, apparently insignificant at the time, that has changed the entire course of his life. As for me, but for this little coincidence I might never have gone back to Holland with all of its trials and tribulations; I might never have become involved in state politics, and I might never have sat in some of the higher councils of medicine.

But in that classroom at Lebanon that day I did not philosophize. I knew I had to have an education, and to get it, I had to have money. Necessity dictated.

So I took the Holland teaching position.

Prospects were not bright for a boy of modest means to become a doctor, and the indications were that if and when he became a doctor he would have a hard time keeping up with what was going on in his profession.

I would like to clarify these points.

First, the gay '90s were not as gay as one might think today.

Wages and commodity prices were low. Markets were demoralized; unemployment was widespread. To a minority it might have been a gay decade, but to the masses it was an era of abject misery and despair, truly a time of conflict and readjustment, a period which saw the widening of the breach between capital and labor.

It was a time of change in social customs. Men gave up their whiskers and discarded their derbies. The ladies let their topknots come down and grew bangs; they threw away their hoop skirts and bustles. Companionate education, commonly called coeducation today, brought both sexes to the same campus.

It was an era when education, and especially medical

education, was making great strides. Public education, which had offered school years of three to seven months between the ages of nine and seventeen, was being extended somewhat. Prior to 1890 the required course in most medical schools consisted of two terms of five months each with practically no entrance requirements except a fair knowledge of the three Rs. In the '90s, as public school education became better, the entrance requirements for medical schools became stricter.

And medicine and surgery were making progress. The young man who entered medical school knew that by the time he came out, many of the things he had learned would be obsolete and he would face the necessity of catching up.

This prospect did not deter me.

"SNUFF HER, DOC, SNUFF HER!"

I ARRIVED in Holland some weeks before the opening of school. I had to take a Texas teachers' examination at Belton, county seat of Bell County. I ran into the school superintendent, and he said, "They'll bust you on Texas history." A couple of days before the examination I bought a copy of Pennybacker's history of Texas and read it. I had a good memory and I crammed for the examination. The examiners gave me 100 on my paper and a four-year certificate to teach in Texas.

It was still some time before the opening of the school term, and my finances were running low. So I joined up with a cousin and went cotton picking in Williamson County, adjoining Bell on the south. There was one way of telling whether a farmer needed hands, without talking to him. That was to look at his cotton wagon out in the field. If there was an empty cotton sack draped over the sideboards of the wagon it was a signal that he wanted pickers. Near Corn Hill we saw such a help-wanted ad, and the farmer engaged us immediately we applied. Already picking on the same farm was a boy by the name of Richard Critz. Years later he became an associate justice of the Texas State Supreme Court. His father was a prosperous Houston,

Mississippi, lawyer, who believed in his son's having to make his own way. So Dick was picking cotton to earn money to continue his law studies. We were brothers under the skin. I was earning money so I eventually could take up my medical studies. Before I returned to Holland I was paid four $20 gold pieces for my picking.

The town of Holland started out as two little settlements, one called Holland and the other Mountain Home. They were a mile or two apart. When the Missouri, Kansas & Texas Railroad (the Katy) built through there in the '80s the line was run betwixt and between the two hamlets. So Holland and Mountain Home just pulled up stakes, moved over to the railroad tracks, merged, and finally called themselves the town of Holland. They dropped "Mountain Home" because there already was a town in Texas by that name, and there wasn't a mountain in sight anyway. So they called it Holland, not for The Netherlands, but for a ginner or merchant who had settled there.

I suppose the town counted a couple hundred souls. There were several stores, a drugstore, a blacksmith shop, a livery stable, lumberyard, school building, a little theater and opera house, an art colony, a women's club and two or three saloons.

There were several characters of note in and around Holland, and I'd like to introduce them to you.

There was old Bachelor Jim. He lived on the edge of the village, on an eighty-acre cotton farm adjoining my uncle's place, where I was boarding. Jim had drifted in when the railroad was built and bought his acreage when land was cheap. He led a lonesome life.

So far as I know, old Jim never intentionally harmed anyone. He paid his debts, chewed tobacco and drank good whisky, but never got drunk.

The first time I ran across him and asked him how he was he stopped dead in his tracks, looked up at the sky, and said, "It looks like we are going to have some kind of weather." I was told that it was just a mannerism of his and that the neighbors had been greeted that way for years. Regardless of whether the sky was blue or overcast, Bachelor Jim would remark, "It looks like we are going to have some kind of weather."

Another character thereabouts was Boozer Jackson, a ranchman, whom I came to know soon after my arrival in Holland. I don't know where he got that given name. Maybe it was a nickname, perhaps a relic of his younger days. At any rate, when I knew him he was not overly given to booze.

He was not well, I can say that. He complained of "attacks of indigestion," a common misnomer in those days for heart attacks. He changed doctors several times. Each of them wanted him to go to a hospital for a thorough examination, but Boozer said he couldn't stay away from his cow critters long enough to make the trip to the city and, anyway, he didn't "have no use for a horsepital."

"Tell you what, Doc," he'd say when his physician pressed the matter, "I'll bet you the best saddle horse I've got agin yourn that I'll live longer than a whole pack o' doctors."

Boozer was a good judge of horseflesh. Anyway no one was going to wager anything. Some of those scrawny cow-men lived to a ripe old age.

To the north and east of Holland there were mostly Scotch-Irish cattlemen and farmers. Among them were quite a few Mississippians, Tennesseans, Georgians and Alabamians. I suppose they had just followed Davy Crockett's trail. To the south and west there were many Germans and Bohemians. These people always had an eye for good black land, and they were partial to farming rather than cattle raising.

A unique feature of the landscape was a thirty-mile-long hedge of bois d'arc stretching from near Belton to Taylor. Bois d'arc is known in other parts of our country as Osage orange. Indians used the hard, flexible limbs for bows, hence the French "bois d'arc." The branches are very thorny and when the trees are planted close together they make a fairly good substitute for a barbed-wire fence. The pale-green fruit of the tree is about the size of a large orange, but badly pock-marked. The juice of the Osage orange is a sticky milklike substance. Sometimes gangs of boys hurled these oranges in mock battles. When the missiles found their mark they made a mess that no mother could love.

How this long hedge came to be in this part of Texas is the subject of various theories. Some say it was planted by a Mexican ranchman, under Spanish domination, as a boundary for his cattle domain. The thorny branches kept his cattle from straying beyond the line.

This hedge ran right behind the Holland school building, and we used the branches to keep some of our pupils in the strait and narrow path of good behavior. It was customary for the culprit to be required to go down to the hedge and cut the switches with which he was to be whipped.

From a teaching position in the four-room school I was promoted to principal during the course of the year. I found it less trying than my school work had been in Mississippi.

Among the many students who gave me no trouble was a bright, beautiful, vivacious girl, about seventeen. I was twenty-four. Her name was Roberta Eugenia Wiseman. She was an orphan. Her mother had died when she was three; her father was killed in a feud when she was six. She was reared by her grandmother and an uncle, Cal. W. Wilson of Holland.

She looked to me like the kind of girl who would make some man a good wife. I couldn't entertain the idea because if a newly arrived professor had started courting one of his pupils the Stinkfinger Gang probably would have run him out of town. And my work came first—until I finished my medical education, anyhow.

One night a character drifted into town who was to have a great deal of influence on my career.

He arrived on the midnight train. No one knew whence he came, nor why. He staggered to a doctor's office, but the doctor was away. The doctor's office had a cot, no other furniture, in an old frame building. The stranger flopped down on the cot. The night marshal took one look at him and said he was drunk.

The next afternoon some fellow reported that the stranger was still on the cot, and that he either was dead or dead drunk.

Finally the doctor examined the man. The doctor said, "He's got typhoid fever." The patient's teeth were covered by a nasty film, his lips were dry, he was dirty and he smelled like the very devil. The doctor told me that if I would attend to the nursing he would see what he could do for the stranger, medically.

Still we had no idea who he was. He had no papers. There was one clue. He was carrying a thermometer of a type which had just come into use, and that led us to believe that he might be a doctor.

He was delirious and he raved all that night. He kept

yelling, "That's a Wall—shoot him, shoot him. That's a Wall—shoot him."

That gave us another clue. I had been reading in the newspapers about a feud at St. Augustine, deep in East Texas. Participating in the feud, which took several lives, were two families by the names of Wall and Border.

The telephone, just coming into use between towns, came in handy. I telephoned the sheriff at St. Augustine, about two hundred miles away, and described our unidentified patient—a man twenty-five to thirty years old, a bullet scar on his left arm, and a fever thermometer on his person.

"Aw hell," said the sheriff, "that's Dr. George Border. The family has been involved in a feud here. His folks live here, and I'll get his mother right away."

After a while the sheriff called back and put Mrs. Border on the phone. Arrangements were made to get a male nurse for Border. And we finally got him on his feet again.

When he got well, Border—his full name was George Fowler Border—decided that then and there would be a good time and place to open a doctor's office. The eighty-year-old doctor who had been his host in Holland was preparing to leave for the Oklahoma Indian Territory, and it was arranged for Border to take over his practice in Holland.

I helped Border obtain the essential instruments and some meager furniture for his office. Also I assisted him in some minor surgery. He built up a fair practice although there was considerable competition. After a while he began urging me to take over his practice because he wanted to join a friend of his who also had gone up into the Indian Territory.

"I'll hold this thing down," he said, "until you get your license to practice and then you take over."

I thought it was a good idea.

At that time one could begin practice by passing an examination before a district medical board after the junior year in medical college.

I chose the Hospital College of Medicine of Central University, Louisville, Kentucky. This medical college, one of the leading institutions of the country at the time, eventually became part of the University of Louisville. I got a rating as a junior there because I had a B.S. degree from National Normal.

At Louisville I had the privilege of studying under Dr. L. S. McMurtry, who held the chair of gynecology and abdominal surgery. He was a Kentuckian of the old school, a gentleman and a scholar. Later, about 1905, he served as president of the American Medical Association. The AMA's council on medical education was established in 1904, and Dr. McMurtry had a great deal to do with the betterment of medical schools.

There was room for improvement. My college year consisted of five months, a little more than half the time you get today in universities. There was not much preparation in the way of biology, zoology and chemistry. We got a smattering of pathology and bacteriology. Our instructors stressed anatomy, physiology and materia medica (remedial substances).

Many medical colleges were proprietary, owned by the group of doctors composing the faculty. Tuition was one hundred dollars or so a year.

We had a good anatomical laboratory, but many of the boys were partial to an anatomy professor who was holding forth at a competing college. He had a rather large class and a few of us at a time would sneak into the pavilion where he was lecturing. We felt a bit as you feel in church without a coin to drop into the collection plate. But any scruples we had about taking something for nothing that others were paying for soon were overshadowed by the professor's erudition and eloquence.

He had a sense of humor, too. He let us sneak into his class a few times without letting on that he knew what was going on. One day when we were all seated, ready to steal from the Pierian spring, the professor said, "Gentlemen, we'll have a fifteen-minute quiz to see what you've learned in two weeks." Then he shot a bunch of questions. He made monkeys out of the poachers who had not attended regularly. He picked on us especially, and when the session became farcical he said very apologetically, "I'm sorry, Gentlemen, I thought you belonged to this class." He didn't mind, though, really.

After my first school year at Louisville I returned to Mississippi for a visit.

It was then that I saw Brother Bob the last time. He was teaching at Mississippi Normal College. He came to see me, and we went to the old Cave Hill cemetery. My hobby was, and is, collecting epitaphs. As we wandered around the old cemetery Bob and I talked about our boyhood and about our ambitions. Each of us had earned his way in school, and it had not been necessary to invoke the boyhood pact we had made to help each other out. We still had our eyes on the big city, though, where he was going to be a great lawyer and I a great surgeon.

I went to Texarkana, Texas, to take my examination to practice medicine and surgery in Texas. As I have indicated, that was permissible those days, even before you finished your medical course. My older brother returned to his teaching position at Mississippi Normal.

Bob died shortly thereafter. Typhoid.

After passing my examination in Texarkana I went back to Holland, ready to take over Dr. Border's practice. On credit I bought an emergency bag, a kit of instruments and a portable sterilizer. Also there was available from Dr. Border a full set of practically unused operating instruments.

So I set up my office upstairs in a vacant building at the fabulous monthly rental of four dollars. But the landlord wanted that four dollars in advance. I resented the implication that I could not make four dollars a month when I was under the necessity of earning several hundred dollars in order to go back to medical school. But I swallowed my pride and buckled down to work.

There were four or five doctors in Holland at that time. The grand old man of medicine was Dr. E. D. Taylor. He was not a drinking man, which was not something that could be said of all doctors in Texas at that time. He had come to Holland in the '80s, when the railroad was built. He taught in the Baptist Sunday School. Also he was a Mason; he taught me the principles of masonry and I felt very kindly toward him.

There were many cases of lobar pneumonia, diagnosed as typho-pneumonia. The death rate was high. Many survivors suffered fever, cough and difficult breathing.

The situation looked ready-made for me.

But I found it hard to break in. There was bias in favor of the old doctor and prejudice against the young doctor who had not completed his studies. It was during this period that I removed the pregnant-like tumor from Aunt Bess, as I have related.

One day an old lady whose son was ill said to me, "Look here, young fellow, we sent for you because we could not find our regular doctor. We want him if this boy has pneumony. He can cure any case that don't run into typho-pneumony."

I asked, "Why can't he cure that?"

The old lady looked at me as if I had hit her with a brick and said, "Any fool ought to know that. Why, that's two deseases in one and what the doctor gives to cure one will aggervate the other."

That was an argument I could not meet.

However, I discovered that the so-called typho-pneumonia was simply post-pneumonia or pleural empyema. That is a collection of pus in the delicate membrane of the lungs. I operated on several cases, draining quarts of pus from the pleural cavity. After I had demonstrated some degree of competence I picked up quite a few cases, got paid for them, too, and was about ready to return to medical school.

About that time there arrived in Holland a case of surgical instruments consigned to two doctors who had left for Tulsa. It was C.O.D. They wired me to pay the bill and forward the instruments to Tulsa, which I did. Then I had a bad debt on my hands. I banked most of the remainder of my earnings. Good thing I did, too, or I might have lost it all in a holdup.

One thing after another delayed my departure. Then I made what I thought was going to be my last call, about five a. m., out on the prairie west of town. It was a crisp, invigorating morning. Coming back I rode toward the most gorgeous sunrise I had ever seen. The eastern horizon was a fiery red, and the sun came up in a blaze of glory and splendor far beyond my ability to describe.

The cowpokes and farmers came into town to do their weekend trading, drinking, fighting, and predicting the weather. For some reason or other, there was pretty general agreement that there was going to be a blizzard—a cold norther.

But just at that time I could not be bothered about a Texas blizzard. I was scheduled to leave on the noon train the following day, headed back to medical school. The temperature kept dropping, but I reassured myself that no matter how cold it got in Texas I would be out of it soon.

By midnight it was 10 degrees above zero, a long-time record for that part of the state. It was a dry cold, very little wind and no clouds. Cattle drifted to the shelter of the bois d'arc hedge, but it gave little protection from the bitter cold.

While I was finding some comfort in the thought that I soon would be out of it, I was called to attend a labor case out on the prairie. The people were tenant farmers, and strangers to me. The distracted father had come to town for me after the doctor he had spoken to previously failed to show up. Maybe it was too cold for him. This farmer's plea was so urgent and his distress so apparent that I did not hesitate to make the call. But I knew I had only twelve hours between that time and the hour of my departure for college.

I found a young woman in labor with her first baby. The house was a mere shack with a leanto, all of thin walls with cracks big enough for a cat to crawl through. An old wood stove furnished some heat. A kerosene lamp gave an eerie, dim light. Water was scarce. The rainwater barrel, almost empty anyway, was frozen solid. The husband walked a half mile to a neighbor's house for a bucket of water. When he returned there was an inch of ice on it.

Every facility for clean obstetrical practice was missing. However, I did the best I could with what I had and with what I knew. I found that I would be stuck for several hours, with my train departure not many hours away.

The furniture in the house was limited. There was one bed; one old rocking chair which Grandma had taken; two plain chairs with cowhide bottoms, and an old wall clock of the Regulator brand. That was one time when I became a clock watcher. Those hands moved too fast . . . three a. m., four . . . five . . . six. The patient's progress was slow. Six hours until that Katy train would pull out, and here I was, ten miles out on the bleak prairie.

I stepped outside to see about the horse I had ridden. I was depending on that animal to take me back. He had been tethered on the south side of the leanto, and the farmer had been thoughtful enough to cover him with a wagon sheet.

I began to think of some safe way to end the case and to wipe off that look of disgust so evident on Grandma's face. She, too, had been waiting for hours. I remember her as if it were only yesterday. When I first arrived at the shack she was sitting in the creaky rocker, rocking very slowly, almost in cadence with that old Regulator. She rolled her snuff brush meditatively, as contented as an old cow chewing her cud.

But as the hours wore on and nothing happened, Grandma began rocking furiously. She massaged her gums with the snuff brush. The end of the brush had been chewed to a frazzle.

When I went back into the refrigerated shack, after tending my horse, Grandma gave me another hard look and said:

"Young feller, I know you ain't had much experience and you need a heap o' larnin'. I will tell you what old Dr. Smith would do. He would snuff her—that's what he would do."

I had no idea what she meant. There were only two kinds of snuff I knew. One was to snuff a candle; the other was snuff dipping. I just simply could not see how either of those snuffs could have anything to do with childbirth.

But I didn't want to let her know that I did not know what she meant.

I was preparing to make what I hoped would be a final examination when Grandma, growing more impatient by the moment, announced firmly, "I think you ought to snuff her."

Still I did not know what the old lady meant. Maybe I was too preoccupied with the Regulator, which ran so fast; with the baby, who seemed so slow in arriving, and with the fast northbound Katy train that was to take me back to college. But I didn't let on.

"Snuff her, Doc, snuff her!" the old lady demanded.

I said, "OK, but you will have to do the snuffing."

Grandma popped up out of the rocker, laid her snuff cud aside and disappeared into the leanto. In a moment she was back with a long pipestem full of powdery snuff. Like an old bellows, Grandma filled her lungs with air, stuck the pipestem in her mouth, got down at the bedside and blew the snuff into both nostrils of my patient.

Soon there was a violent seizure of sneezing, and a ten-pound boy made his appearance.

And soon thereafter I was back on my horse, headed for

town and that Katy train. I boarded the train with some medical books in one hand and a six-bit canvas, telescope-type suitcase in the other.

I was ready to agree with the old crone that what I needed was "a heap o' larnin'." But there were some more practical experiences in store for me before I got back to the lecture room and laboratory.

I have told how two doctors who had left Holland for Tulsa became indebted to me. They had asked me to pay the C.O.D. charges on a case of surgical instruments and to forward the equipment to them. It amounted to $150. Now, I needed that money for college expenses. They didn't have the ready cash, but they advised me that if I would come on up there and perform an operation, the fee would pay their debt to me. So I decided to go to Louisville by way of Tulsa. The doctors arranged for the operation in an Indian home on the outskirts of the town.

The trip to Oklahoma City was in the face of a blizzard, the same blizzard that had hit Texas the night before while I was helping to "snuff" a baby into this world. When we entered the Oklahoma territory the thermometer was reported at 20 degrees below zero. It was impossible to keep the coaches warm; when trainmen turned sufficient steam into the radiators there was not enough power left to pull the train. They finally put on another engine, and then another. With three engines we had some warmth and finally pulled into Oklahoma City.

There was a six-hour layover. I went to an old frame hotel near the station. It was too cold to try to sleep, and I couldn't spare the money anyway. I hugged the old pot-bellied stove in the hotel lobby until train time. I arrived in Tulsa about noon. I suppose the town had a population of 1,500 to 2,000 at that time, but there were very few people on the street. The temperature was 30 degrees below zero. The sky was as clear as crystal.

The doctors had a small office in the back end of a frame building where an Irishman was running a drugstore which in reality was a blind for illegal whisky. The operation was set for nine a. m. of the following day. I spent another cold and sleepless night with one of the doctors, who lived in a small frame building in the rear of the so-called drugstore.

The partner I was staying with was a bachelor. I learned from him that he and his associate were on very bad terms. My first impulse was to have nothing to do with the planned surgery, but finding that it was a matter of urgency and necessity, I decided to go along.

All preparations had been made for home, or so-called kitchen-table, surgery. The three of us arrived at the modest home promptly at nine a. m. The mercury still showed thirty degrees below zero.

I checked the patient's lungs and heart after she had been placed on the table. Everything seemed to be in good order, ready for the operation.

One of the doctors began giving the patient chloroform while the other doctor and I scrubbed our hands. I happened to look in on the patient and saw that she was not breathing. The doctor had dropped off to sleep and the chloroform was spilling onto the mask over her face.

The two of us tried to bring the patient back to life by artificial respiration, heart-stimulation, by drugs and external massage of the heart. The more modern method of cutting to the heart and massaging it by hand was far in the future at that time. Anyway, all our efforts were useless and the good lady passed on to join the tribal dead in their happy hunting ground.

While we were gathering up our instruments and paraphernalia and trying to comfort the family of the deceased, the anesthetist sobered up enough to slip out of the house. He went into town and told the loafers around the drugstore-grogshop that the doctor from Texas and his partner had killed a woman. By the time we arrived at the Irishman's whisky mill the mob around there was in a rather ugly mood.

We talked to the town marshal and asked him to go out to the squaw's house and investigate what had happened. While the marshal was busy with the case, the anesthetist who had bungled the job and killed the patient with chloroform rode off southward. He was next heard of in Mexico. The family exonerated the other doctor and me of all blame, but they failed to pay us for the services we had rendered. I needed the money, but I did not blame the family for not paying. I got something out of it, though—I learned a lesson worth a million times the $150 I expected to get out of the operation. The experience taught me never to place my faith in just anyone as an anesthetist, and never to assume responsibility in a surgical procedure unless I was in full control.

After that episode, I was more than ready to leave Tulsa. They told me at the station that there would not be any passenger trains for several days. The cold weather seemed to be getting worse. At four p. m. it was 33 degrees below zero.

There was a small, red-whiskered tough-looking fellow

hanging around the drugstore. The druggist introduced him to me as "Red Watson." After dark, when Red left with his saddlebags full of liquor, the druggist told me that Red was a scout for the Al Jennings gang. He said the gang was holed up in the hills about two miles from town. The revenuers were after them and the deputy marshals were expected at any time. I had heard of the Al Jennings gang, but was not expecting to see them so soon. Early the next morning old Red came into town again. He tied his sprig-tailed roan pony to a post back of the drugstore. When Red came to the front and peeked out he saw the marshal's horses tied to the hitching rack in front of the big frame hotel up the street. Red ran like a wild man, jumped on his pony and pulled out.

I asked the druggist what happened to Red. He said Red had gone to tell the gang that the marshals and the revenuers were in town. I thought, of course, that I had seen the last of the Jennings boys, that they probably would withdraw deeper into the hills.

I was not prepared for what followed. From some distance there came the thunder of horses' hoofs. Then there was yelling, shooting and the clatter of many horses' feet on the frozen ground of the one-street town. I looked out through a crack in the front door of the drugstore. I saw a red-headed, medium-sized man leading the gang. He had the bridle reins between his teeth and a six-shooter in each hand. The gang was strung out behind him. Otherwise there was not a living creature in sight. They swept by the hitching rack, shot under the feet of several tethered horses and made the animals break loose and run off. They shouted curses at the officers and told them to get out of town or come out and fight. After a while the gang rode out of town without incident. The officers rounded up their runaway horses and rode away.

I would have ridden away, too, if I had had a horse. I went back to the station. I found that a cattle train was being made up for St. Louis. A hog raiser had two carloads of hogs to go. He was entitled to a pass to ride in the caboose so he could take care of his hogs en route to St. Louis. I overheard the hog raiser tell the railroad agent that it was too cold to make a trip on a freight train to St. Louis. I saw a way to get out of Tulsa and on my way to college.

So I proposed to look after his hogs if he would give me his pass. We traded pronto. The two carloads of hogs were switched into the middle of the train, there being about twenty cars of cattle between the caboose and the hogs.

About two o'clock in the afternoon, we headed north, with three locomotives pulling the train. Progress was slow. There were five cowboys in the caboose. They were loaded with bad whisky and were in a fussy mood. They started a poker game. Finally they invited me to join in the game. When I refused, they became very offensive and began calling me names which in my day and in my community were fighting words. They also called me a hog drover and began singing a vulgar parody on the current song, "Hog drovers, hog drovers we are, courting your daughters so beautiful and fair."

When I told them I had no money and did not know how to play poker they proposed to bet me a car of cattle against my two cars of hogs. I finally had to take refuge in the cupola of the caboose where the brakeman already had fled after the cow waddies got too tough for him. The brakeman slipped me an iron poker, which he had hidden in his pants leg, and told me to "let 'em have it" if they tried to haul us down out of the cupola.

But a train wreck solved our problem. As we neared Springfield, Missouri, along about midnight, our train stalled at a railroad intersection. Another freight train came along and rammed the middle of our train about two cars back of my hogs. Several cars were derailed and cattle scattered everywhere. That ended the feud with the cowboys. Their part of the train was cut off.

After many hours' delay we resumed our journey northward. During the long ride I decided that I should take a look at my hogs. There still were several cattle cars between the caboose and the hog cars. When the train stopped I stepped from the caboose and walked forward to the hogs. Before I realized what was going on, the train started again. I knew I could not get back to the caboose, so I grabbed the ladder handholds used by the brakeman and climbed on top of a car. But there was ice all over the tops of the cars and I knew I could not make it back to the caboose, so I sat with my legs around the brake rod and with my back to the wind. It was more than an hour before the train stopped again. By that time I was so stiff that when I tried to climb off I fell off and rolled over into the snow drift alongside the railroad embankment. A brakeman saw me and came to my rescue. I told him why I was there and where I belonged. He helped me back to the caboose and said, "Let them darned hogs alone—if they freeze to death they will bring as much dead as alive because they are headed for the slaughterhouse anyway."

That eased my conscience and I settled down for a peaceful ride into East St. Louis. The broker met me at the stockyards. I delivered the bill of lading for the two carloads of hogs and he gave me a receipt. That closed my career as a drover.

It was late at night and bitterly cold. The owl car, the last of the night to leave East St. Louis for the city, was about to pull out. I boarded it along with several others. We had just crossed the river when a bandit boarded the car, ordered everyone to stand up and proceeded to take everything of value. I had thirty dollars in my purse and a cheap watch. The robber took it all. But I had five dollars in my shoe which he failed to get.

I landed at Union Station in St. Louis. For five nights I had had only catnaps. I had five dollars and was hungry. And that was the very last day I had to reach my destination in order to enroll for my final year in medical college. The train for Louisville left at eight a. m. The fare was nine dollars. There was not time to wire home for money. I had nothing to pawn but my clothes and they were not worth nine dollars, nor even four dollars.

There was a row of ticket-scalper shops down the street outside the station. I found a return ticket to Louisville. I bought the ticket for $4.75 without looking it over. That left me a quarter. I was cold and hungry. I bought a cup of coffee, five cents; and two doughnuts, five cents. I made a rush for the train and was on my way.

I slept in the smoker where I found the only vacant seat. After a while the conductor shook me, and said, "Ticket, please." Nonchalantly I handed him my $4.75 ticket, still congratulating myself that I had saved enough money from the robbery to buy the cheap-rate ticket.

The conductor looked at the ticket, then at me, and asked me my name. I had not noticed that the name "Bowers" was signed on the back of the ticket, so I told him my right name. Never before, and never since then, have I found myself under circumstances where I thought it necessary to change my name.

But changing my name then would not have done any good anyway. It seems that the ticket described this fellow Bowers as bald-headed, red-faced, height five feet ten, weight 240 pounds. I had a mop of hair, was pale, six feet three inches tall and weighed 130.

The conductor said, "Son, you will have to get off at the next stop or pay your fare."

It was a hundred miles to the next stop. When the conductor came through the next time I decided to come clean. I told him the story of my experiences in Tulsa, the robbery in East St. Louis and that I had only a few hours until my deadline at medical college. I suggested that evidently someone had a ride coming on that scalper ticket and since Mr. Bowers weighed 240 pounds and I weighed only 130 the railway company would have 110 pounds less weight to haul if they took me instead of Bowers. The conductor was not particularly impressed but he said, "OK, Buddy, but you will have a hard time with the conductor who takes over at the next stop." He kept the ticket and just before we got into the terminal where they changed train crews, the old conductor came in, placed a through check in my hatband, and said, "Keep your seat and good luck!"

You know, since then I have always felt kindly toward all conductors.

And then and there I celebrated. I bought two doughnuts and three apples for a dime. That left me a nickel to pay my streetcar fare to Mother Redding's boardinghouse when the train arrived in Louisville. There I was not a stranger and I arranged temporary financing until I could get some of my funds from Holland.

Returning to medical college as a senior I enjoyed certain prerogatives.

In our anatomy laboratory each group of eight students got one cadaver. I headed my group; that is, I was the prosector. It was my job to dissect and expose each tissue to show where it started, where it ended and to explain its function.

There were societies which opposed human mutilation, as they called it. Members used to drop into our laboratory and make an eyewitness report on what those young brutes out at the college were doing. No doubt those people were well intentioned, but they got to where they were a nuisance.

One day a whole delegation came in and moved freely about the laboratory while four or five groups of students were working on as many cadavers. In spite of the annoyance, some of our boys appeared to be particularly amiable, going out of their way to do a lot of backslapping and that sort of thing.

A short time after the visitors left, a committee of them came back for an indignation conference with the college authorities. It seems that the visitors had found miscellaneous human fingers, toes and ears in their pockets. There was a strong suspicion that the brutes had slipped these things into the pockets. By that time, though, the cadavers had been pretty well cut up and it was impossible to prove that the parts came from the college laboratory. We came clear, if not clean.

I was in my last year of medical school when the battleship Maine blew up. That was the Pearl Harbor of the Spanish-American War of 1898. The American ship had anchored in Cuban, or Spanish, waters. There was an explosion, attributed to a mine, and more than two hundred lives were lost. Excitement ran high and resentment against the Spanish government was furious.

Along with other students, I went downtown to get the latest news. The *Courier-Journal* was putting out an extra every hour.

A boy came out of the basement of the Courier-Journal building with a batch of papers. I bought one and tendered a silver dollar. That was all the money I had with me, and a good percentage of my total cash resources. He handed me a paper and told me he would go and get the change. I told him to leave his papers with me as security until he returned with the change. He did so, and promptly disappeared with my dollar, never to return. I soon realized I had bought a dollar's worth of extras instead of one copy. I was on a strict and close budget, and could not afford to lose the change. So, for the time being, I became a newsboy. But customers were grabbing the papers, and I sold out in ten minutes or less.

I learned a lesson there that, it occurred to me later, I should have learned long before that. That was: Always trust a newsboy, or any boy, so far as that goes. I invited that boy to do what he did. Never place a boy in a position where you let him know you don't trust him.

The experience in Louisville underscored what happened years previously when I instituted self-government in the Friendship school.

The night my medical class graduated, as the dean, Dr. P. Richard Taylor, was handing out the diplomas, the band played a popular tune of the time, which went something like this: "Oh, Mr. Johnson, turn me loose, I have got no money, but a good excuse." That fit me exactly.

By the time I graduated the shooting with Spain was over. I finished with honors and was awarded an internship, but was unable to accept it because I had volunteered to enter the armed forces as a contract surgeon with the occupation troops in the Philippines.

War activity had run in the family, so to speak. A Crosthwait was an officer in the Revolutionary War; they were in the War Between the States, and another was a lieutenant-colonel in the Indian Wars and in the War of 1812.

I was ordered to San Antonio, Texas, for examination and induction. I spent several days there at Fort Sam Houston taking examinations. Then came the final day when I had to take my physical examination.

A short, fat captain looked me over briefly and said "Heck, fellow, you'll die before you get to the Philippines."

So I was rejected.

I was never quite sure whether my rejection was on account of my ignorance or my health. I did look bad, sallow-complexioned and thin as a rail. My failure to make the grade was a disappointment which was not to be erased until years later when I served as a neurosurgeon in World War I.

There was nothing for me to do except resume practice at Holland.

I had six cents and a bronchial cough. I still have the cough.

I made my way to Holland somehow or other, arriving there about noon on a Sunday.

That same afternoon two young mothers were buried

in the town cemetery. I attended the services with some of my relatives. They told me that there were twenty-three practically new graves in that cemetery and that most of them were the result of childbed fever.

Later that afternoon I called to see my first patient since graduating from medical school. She was a young mother with a four-day-old baby. She was critically ill, and frightened almost to the stage of shock and hysteria. She had a high temperature, rapid pulse, periodical chills and backache.

I had never seen a case of puerperal infection (childbed fever) before.

I spent a sleepless night, and was back on my case early the next morning. We had no sulpha drugs, no penicillin, and it was long before the days of blood transfusion. We did have the so-called antiseptic drugs—carbolic acid, mercury drugs, permanganate of potassium, iodine, pure grain alcohol and others. Just out of college, I was well grounded in antiseptic technique.

I made use of this knowledge and of the drugs at my disposal. Slowly the patient recovered. She is alive after fifty-six years, and is still listed among my patients.

Soon I had more obstetrical cases than I could take care of. I formed a partnership with another young doctor, Dr. Charles Walter Goddard, who years later became Texas state health officer. Gradually I began to concentrate on surgery.

Maybe it was a bit ironical, but one of my first jobs as a surgeon was to work on a corpse. It was almost like being back in medical college dissecting cadavers. I am going to relate my experience as an indication of the jack-of-all-trades the pioneer doctor was.

On a hot Saturday afternoon in August, 1899, there was a funeral at a nearby cemetery. One of the village belles had died, under rather strange circumstances, in the city. Her body was brought back to the hometown cemetery and laid to rest in the family plot.

Even then, at the funeral, there were whispered rumors about the cause of her death.

On Sunday morning I received a telegram from the district judge of a nearby county instructing me to procure whatever help was necessary to exhume the body. I was ordered to perform an autopsy, remove certain specimens from the body and to appear before the grand jury with the evidence, the following morning.

I hired two Negro laborers to open the grave. With the help of two onlookers, they lifted the casket to the surface. It was the poorest job of embalming I ever smelled. The Negroes took to their heels and never returned to fill up the grave. A local doctor, who had retired, was to help me. He fainted. An undertaker and his helper, a young man who was anxious to become a doctor, stood by for a while. The young man fled, and that was the end of his medical career.

That left me and the undertaker at the grave. I placed two specimens in a fruit jar filled with preservative. Now it was up to us to rebury the corpse. But the undertaker was an old man, and I had to do most of the shoveling.

Stiff in the joints, I appeared the next morning before the grand jury to testify as to what I had found. A prominent young doctor, who was somewhat of a ladies' man but a bungler as a surgeon, had undertaken to operate on the girl, who had been "showing." The doctor was indicted on charges of murder and other offenses.

At the trial both the defense and the prosecution were represented by very able counsel.

I was given a pretty severe going over by both sides. After I had testified I was released from the rule requiring witnesses to remain outside the courtroom, and was permitted to remain in the room while other witnesses testified.

At noon recess while I was at lunch at the hotel a brother of the deceased came and sat at the table with me. I knew him quite well. I noticed he was very nervous and pale and that he was "toting," as they say, a .45-caliber six-shooter.

I asked him what he was going to do with that gun. He said he was going to kill that so-and-so doctor. I told him not to do that because the jury probably would hang him anyway. The outraged brother insisted that he was going to avenge his sister's death.

I hurried back to the courthouse and told the doctor's attorney what the brother had said. The attorney told the defendant, who said, "He don't have the guts to do a thing like that."

When court resumed after the noon recess the prisoner was sitting next to a former Texas ranger and was flanked by his two attorneys. I just happened to be seated on the bench directly behind the prisoner.

The last state witness was testifying as to the gruesome happenings in the operating room where the girl died when I had a premonition that something terrible was about to happen.

I glanced back over my shoulder and saw the brother of the dead girl approaching. He was as white as a sheet and was holding his six-shooter in his trembling hand. He walked briskly until he got just behind me. Then he fired over my left shoulder and hit the prisoner in the back.

He fired only once, but, you know, those old guns, called hog-legs, made a noise like a cannon and smoked like a burning tar bucket.

The gunman turned and ran toward the door. The ex-ranger drew one of his guns and fired at the fleeing man, but he missed. The bullet knocked about a bushel of plaster off the courtroom wall. The doorway was jammed with people and the gunman could not get out that way for the moment. He ran over to a window. The ex-ranger fired again and shattered the window pane. Slivers of glass showered the place.

By that time the tiny courtroom was filled with plaster dust and gunpowder smoke. When things cleared up a bit, the courtroom, which had been packed when the shooting started, was almost empty. The jurors fled down the back stairway and they did not stop until they got across the river. The judge was crouched down behind the bar. The lawyers were under the tables. About the only one who had not moved was the prisoner. The bullet had cut his spinal column and paralyzed him from the waist down.

The man who started the shooting was gone. Incidentally, I don't recall that he ever was arrested.

The wounded doctor, fully conscious, was taken from the courtroom on a stretcher. So we had on hand a man with a bullet in his back and we didn't know just where it had lodged.

That is where the X-ray came in handy. On December 28, 1895 William Conrad Roentgen had announced the discovery of that phenomenon. The announcement was made before the physics society of the University of Würzburg. Physicians were fascinated by the invention of an apparatus which we today accept as commonplace. Among those who went to Germany to learn more about the X-ray was Dr. Robert S. Hyer of Southwestern University, Georgetown, Texas. He was professor of physics and later served as president of the University. From Germany Dr. Hyer brought back an X-ray tube.

When he read about the courtroom shooting and the defendant's paralysis, he asked permission to make a picture. The exposure was on a ten by twelve glass plate. The photograph, though crude as compared with the product of our modern X-ray machines, showed exactly where the bullet was imbedded in the spinal column. The bullet had cut the cord in two. It never regenerates.

So far as I know, that was the first X-ray picture made in Texas for diagnostic purposes. The apparatus was primitive indeed when compared with the many fine machines which, years later, I saw demonstrated at national and international medical meetings.

But at that time and place it served the same purpose that the precision instruments of today serve. Once the bullet was located, it was removed.

The doctor, though, never walked again. His trial was never finished. I suppose the authorities thought he had been punished enough.

AUNT LUCKY AND HER MAGIC JUG

LET'S PAUSE to review my own situation in 1899. I was twenty-six years old. My education had been piecemeal, interrupted by the necessity of earning money to continue my studies. Finally I was awarded the degree of Doctor of Medicine at Louisville, but I served no internship such as is part of the routine of every medical-school graduate today. Partially making up for that deficiency was practice between my junior and senior years in college.

When I returned to Holland, after being graduated at Louisville and being rejected for government service in the Philippines, I was a full-fledged doctor. I could write "M.D." after my name.

The year 1900 was a momentous one in history and in my own career. Let's have a glimpse. . . .

Many young men had just come back from the Spanish-American war. In China the Boxer Rebellion broke out. In South Africa the Boer War was in progress. At home, William Jennings Bryan, the Democratic nominee for president, was defeated by William McKinley, the victim of an assassin's bullet the next year. For Texas, the devastating hurricane at Galveston was the big news event of 1900.

The American Medical Association was fighting legislation designed to forbid the use of animals in scientific experiments.

Real skyscrapers were being planned, and some doctors were worried about the sanitation. They questioned whether disposal facilities would operate efficiently in these tall buildings. Some engineers said the skyscraper was a passing thing anyway, that when the reenforcing iron rusted the whole building would crumple. Sanitarians were calling attention to the fact that Pullman car lavatories provided only one wash basin, and they pointed out there should be a separate basin for cleaning teeth.

In New York the American Society for the Prevention of Premature Burial was incorporated. The organization sought legislation to prevent the burial of persons who were mistaken for dead. At that time there were horror stories in the press about patients who had been buried alive. Two remedial measures were suggested: One, to hold the "corpse" a certain number of hours before burial; or, two, provide the "corpse" with some kind of signal device in the casket.

But to the farmers of our community the greatest menace was the spread of the boll weevil. This insect crossed the Rio Grande from Mexico about 1894, and by 1900 it had spread as far north as central Texas. It left ruination, starvation and death in its wake.

Cotton farmers and cattlemen in central Texas were not too friendly toward each other. The farmer wanted to fence his land to protect his crops from marauding livestock. Many cattlemen wanted their animals to range at large for feed and water. Barbed wire was coming into general use, and it looked like the farmer had the upper hand. Some cattlemen resorted to fence cutting. A law was passed against carrying a pair of pliers. It was all right to carry a pistol in most places, but no pliers.

When the boll weevil came in it looked like this little insect was going to turn the tide of battle between farmer and stockman. Cotton planters suffered while cattlemen prospered.

About sun-up, one clear morning, I was outside feeding my horse. I saw Bachelor Jim running in his cotton field. I saw him stop and heard him holler, "Help, save me!" Then he fell over. I rushed over to see what had happened. His mouth was burned a whitish color, he was blue in the face and was gasping for breath. I found an empty one-ounce bottle labeled "Carbolic Acid."

The ravages of the boll weevil had driven Bachelor Jim to a suicidal impulse.

I yelled to the folks at the house to bring me a bottle of grain alcohol.

I asked Jim, lying between two rows of the cotton, how he felt, but he did not answer. If he could have answered, I am sure he would have said, "It looks like we are going to have some kind of weather."

Before the alcohol arrived, Bachelor Jim was dead.

At the funeral the local preacher hardly knew what to say. Bachelor Jim was not one of the pillars of the church. At that time there was a very definite feeling that church-goers would go to a better world and that nonbelievers were headed elsewhere. But the preacher did manage to say that Bachelor Jim was a good man and that he would not have to worry any more. That sentiment carried with it the idea that wherever he went he never would be plagued again by the boll weevils.

Wherever old Jim is I hope the weather is pleasant.

I've mentioned the ailing Boozer Jackson. After attending his funeral I wrote this ditty:

Don't let the preacher blow me up,
Don't cry when the undertaker lets me down;
I'm not the best and not the worst,
Just an average fellow around your town.

Boozer had been a good trader and a good provider for his family. He was one of the largest contributors to a church which he personally never attended. He left religion to his wife and children.

When old Boozer died he had a big funeral. It was in the springtime. The flowers were in full bloom, the cattle were fat and sleek and everyone was happy. That is with the exception of Boozer and Boozer's family and apparently they were not too much disturbed. The widow would take over, and the oldest boy soon would be twenty-one.

The interment was at the community graveyard. One very tall marble shaft, surrounded by many small, modest slabs, marked the place where the oldest settler, Boozer's grandpa, was buried sixty years previously.

Boozer's funeral was on a Sunday afternoon. Folks came from miles around. They came walking, on horseback, some in buggies and whole families in wagons.

The long funeral cortege slowly wended its way from the house on the hilltop to the quiet cemetery in the valley beside the spring creek. The vehicles moved at a respectful pace, but could not help stirring up a little Texas dust, which settled over an almost new Studebaker wagon at the head of the procession. On that wagon, drawn by four of old Boozer's work mules and driven by his farm foreman, were the mortal remains of the community's first citizen. In the fringe-topped, six-seater surrey rode the widow and seven children—sad, but dry-eyed.

Old Boozer had told them that when he passed on he wanted no wailing and weeping and with them, by gum, his word was law, dead or alive.

Soon the wagon pulled up alongside the grave. Several husky cowboys and ranchmen leaped upon the wagon and lifted the casket out of the heavy pine box. The men atop the wagon handed the casket to eight or ten others on the ground, who placed it beside the grave.

The casket, or coffin, as it was called there, was made of metal, said to have been copper. It had been ordered especially, all the way from Dallas, and was reported to have cost more than a thousand dollars.

The family and near-relatives sat on benches brought from a nearby edifice, which served both as schoolhouse and church.

The local preacher and the deacon stood at opposite ends of the casket; the preacher at the head, the deacon at the foot. I remember some of the minister's words:

"We have come here to pay our last respects to our beloved fellow citizen. It appears right and in order that we open our services with prayer."

Then the deacon was asked to pray:

"Oh Lord, you know, like we know, that this community has lost a good man. He is dead and we are about to cover his body with the earth which he loved so well. Lord, he was not a member of any church, but at heart he was a Christian. He had his good and his bad points; he had his likes and his dislikes; his weak and his strong points. Lord, we know that in the Book of Life many bad things and shortcomings are charged to old Boozer Jackson. Lord, please be sure that he gets full credit for the good things he has done. Please take care of him. He left his family well fixed and they can take care of themselves. Amen."

A group of cowboys then sang a doleful and plaintive ballad of the ranches and prairies which in modern times is entitled "The Last Roundup." Somehow or other, when that piece is played today by a hillbilly guitarist or honky-tonk jukebox, it doesn't sound like it did that day when Boozer Jackson was buried.

A lot of people cried that day, but not the family.

By request of the widow, the cowboys tried to sing "The Old Rugged Cross." They messed that one up. The tenor was riding all over the bass. Besides, they did not know the words, at least not all of them. They mumbled to fill in the gaps. They struggled through a couple of stanzas and then the preacher took over.

I can't recall all he said as he "consigned to the earth the mortal remains of your friend and mine. . . .

"The rich, black earth of his native abode will cover his lifeless form. Winter winds and snows will come and in the springtime the grass and flowers will grow. At night the bugs and beasts will chirp and prowl about his grave. The morning will be greeted by the song of the birds that have nested and reared their young in the shrubbery that will rise above this grave. But there will come no word from our friend for he has had his day and his say."

The minister went on for some time. I remember his closing remarks:

"We leave him now to return to the earth he loved so well and to become a critter in the great herd of humanity who have gone on before and those who must follow, awaiting the great roundup when the last trumpet shall sound."

The cowboys filled up the grave, patted it with the backs of their shovels, and silently rode away.

Old Boozer was gone, along with Bachelor Jim, but there were others whose lives became a part of my experience.

I have told about the gang that initiated me when I first visited Holland in the mid-'90s.

This group, which started out as "the Dirty Dozen," later became known as the "Stinkfinger Gang." Most of them were sons of prominent citizens in the community who had leisure and means to engage in devilment. On Saturday nights they would take a northbound train to Temple where they would shoot craps or play poker until early Sunday morning. Then they would take a train back home just in time to clean up and go to Sunday School.

None of them ever went to college. They held that education was a waste of time. I watched their careers. Most of them turned out all right.

One of them died early in life, so we can count him out.

One became governor-general in a military district under occupation forces following the Spanish-American War. One became an expert chess player. Another became a major league baseball player.

Still another, J. Barton Blair, fell in love with the town belle. He was making slow progress so he got religion and joined the church. Still he made very little headway with the object of his affection. Winter came and went, and he resumed his old antics and associations.

Next time the Molly Bailey Tent Show came to town the gang pulled a stunt that has come to be one of the legends of the community. At that time, "High Life" (carbon disulphide) was a common household item. A drop of it was sufficient to kill bedbugs, to move a balky mule or to send a stray bull back to his own pasture. The Stinkfingers hot-dropped some of the animals in the dog-and-pony show. Pandemonium broke loose on the circus lot. The showmen finally rounded up their animals and left town.

I don't know whether J. Barton Blair had anything to do with it or not, but he was accused as the ringleader. There was a church trial not unlike those we used to have in Mississippi. The defendant was summoned to appear in open meeting and confess his sins and ask forgiveness. Most of the congregation showed up. The church register, opened to the name of J. Barton Blair, lay on the clerk's table. When the defendant's name was called he rose and said:

"Mr. Clerk, from that page so bright and fair,
Please erase the name J. Barton Blair."

And so it was done. Blair lost not only the suit for the girl but his church membership as well.

I would like to add that he lived to be a better and more useful citizen than many of those who sat in judgment on him.

Another member of the Stinkfinger Gang made a reputation—if you want to call it that—as a chili eater. He ran a blacksmith shop in the town, and he was a good blacksmith, but his local fame rested on the fact that three times a day—at ten, two and four o'clock—he left the anvil and forge and headed for the chili parlor. It got so that folks could regulate their clocks and watches by the village smithy's trips to the chili stand.

Hollis Moreland's chili was worth going after. Making chili has become almost a lost art. They call it "chili con carne" these days, which means "peppers with meat," but it is mostly messed up with beans. At Hollis' Chili House you could have your chili with meat only, or you could have beans with it.

I came to relish it, especially on cold mornings. I would order a bowl of chili, and the waiter would yell back to the cook, "One Mexican revolution!" I would add, "No beans, please," and the waiter would yell, "Cut out the ammunition."

Speaking of ammunition:

One day I went into a Holland store to pay a bill. The storekeeper, who had always been friendly, greeted me:

"Doc, I understand you're carrying a gun for me."

I was shocked. And I was startled when I saw a loaded six-shooter lying on his counter.

"If you've got one," he went on, "do you think you're ready to use it?"

"I don't have a gun, and I hadn't given it any thought," I replied, trembling in my boots.

I began looking for the nearest exit, and as I did so I saw a more-or-less familiar figure slink out of the door.

It was Freddie Tickfaw, the bully of Burkett Institute, whom I had thrashed three years previously. He had come to Holland to visit his uncle, the storekeeper.

It finally dawned on me that the vindictive kid had spread a report that I was gunning for the storekeeper.

I explained the matter, and the storekeeper sent his nephew back to Mississippi.

There was another character who came into my life. What her real name was I never knew. They called her Aunt Lucky. She was the neighborhood midwife, family nurse, governess, carrier of gossip and mother confessor. I don't recall that she ever had any children of her own; at least she never mentioned any. Thus all her love and affection and care were spread out among the families of the community. And sometimes she did have to spread it thin to make it go around because many were poor and children were legion.

But whenever anyone was sick or hurt, Aunt Lucky usually was first on the scene. It was before the widespread use of the telephone and I often marveled how Aunt Lucky found out about cases that needed attention. The news must have traveled literally by grapevine; there certainly was more grapevine than telephone wire in that community.

The residents were very considerate of doctors. For one thing, they were reluctant to call on the same doctor repeatedly. Some of them were never able to pay any of us; and, to avoid the embarrassment of sending for a doctor they already owed, they would change doctors every time a new doctor came to town.

Whenever I was called to see a patient, usually at night, Aunt Lucky already was there. So was her big brown jug. Folks thereabouts called it her magic jug.

Almost invariably she had made the diagnosis and would greet me with her conclusion: "Doc, she's got pneumony," or, "Doc, he's got typhoid fever," or, "Doc, that boy's broke out bad with measles."

"Now, Doc," she would jabber without giving me a chance to ask questions, "if you've got with you what it takes to cure, we are lucky. You just leave whatever it takes and I'll carry on from there. If the sick 'un ain't better by tomorrow night we'll send for you."

Usually, with other calls pressing for attention, I was glad enough to leave minor cases in her care. Besides, who was I to say that she should be ousted from a household after she had been admitted, if not invited? After all, she was there before I was. Then, too, I consoled myself with the thought that the psychological effect of her presence might be as beneficial as some of the medicaments I could administer.

And sometimes her magic jug took the place of instruments. I remember at least one such occasion. It was cotton-picking time.

One of the little things that gave doctors a lot of business in those days was cottonseed. A seed of cotton is about the size of a pea covered with fuzz. During the picking season when children, white and black, were out in the fields with their parents, the little ones would amuse themselves by stuffing these seeds in their nostrils. Just one of those playful gestures, and the seed could become a serious obstruction in the nasal passages. Once the seed got into the nostril, the fuzz seemed to give it a sort of animal-like locomotion that sent it deeper and deeper. After some hours the moistened seed would begin to swell, and you had trouble on your hands, especially when your facilities for detection and removal of the seed were so limited. Sometimes surgery became necessary.

Once, when a frightened mother had sent for me, Aunt Lucky's magic jug already had done the job. When I got to the place the child was playing out in the yard. The parents told me that Auntie had given the child a drink from her magic jug, the child was seized with a violent sneezing, and the cottonseeds had popped out of the nostrils like peas out of a peashooter.

You might question the method, but you can't argue with success, and, in that community, whether you were dealing with cottonseed or gallstones, it was not good to challenge Aunt Lucky.

Now, don't jump to conclusions, but that brown jug

looked exactly like many a one I had seen under farmers' beds. In those days, before all shapes and sizes of decanters and bottles came into general use, the saloonkeeper received his whisky in barrels. Many customers had big brown jugs which, from time to time, were refilled from a barrel at the saloon. During prohibition, of course, the fruit jar came into general use as a receptacle of bootleg liquor, but I am talking about the days long before prohibition in Texas. The big brown jug, not "the little brown jug," as the song goes, was pretty generally used for spirits.

Understand, I'm not saying that Aunt Lucky—may she rest in peace!—carried anything alcoholic in her jug. It was not my business to inquire; I was not a revenooer. All I know is that this jug, called the magic jug, went with Aunt Lucky on her rounds just the way my saddlebags went with me and my horse.

Finally, after I gained the confidence of one of the old-timers of the community, I got part of the story of the magic jug.

As soon as the doctor had called, Aunt Lucky would take charge of all medicine left for the patient. In the days of the horseback doctor it was not a matter of telephoning the nearest drugstore to get the prescriptions filled and delivered. Every doctor's saddlebags were filled with seasonable remedies, including tinctures, salves, extracts, powders, decoctions and syrups. I was told that Aunt Lucky would take whatever the doctor had left behind, would drop it into the magic jug, and then would administer liberal doses to the patient from the jug.

She would tell her (or my) patients that, in addition to what Doc had brought, she had something in the jug that was good for anything that could happen to anyone. And if the doctor had made a mistake, she confided, the jug contained what it took to remedy that, too.

And there were times when Aunt Lucky decided the patient didn't need the jug at all. She would just sit and talk. Maybe she would dispense a bit of regional folklore. The story of Rattlesnake Sam and his friend Pete was one of her favorites. Remind me to tell you more of the Sam and Pete story before I finish this narrative.

Aunt Lucky never made any claims that her magic jug was "good for man or beast." There were some quack remedies on the market at the time which were advertised as "good for what ails man or beast." No, sir, Aunt Lucky never catered to animals lower than man, but I'll tell you what did happen.

On Sunday afternoons, while the women were getting on with their knitting, the men usually gathered in a mesquite pasture. They had cleared the brush off of a quarter-mile stretch and there they staged horse races. These animals usually were just cow ponies of mustang origin, from neighboring ranches. One Sunday afternoon one of these quarter horses, the sorriest and scrubbiest of the lot, turned up sick. An old waddy had raced him any number of times and had never won a dime. As I recall it, the name of the horse was Two-Bits; maybe that was just wishful thinking.

Those mustangs usually hung their heads low, even when they were in the best of spirits. On this day Two-Bits drooped down to where he was breathing on the carpet grass. His owner was in about the same attitude. Another cowpoke said that Aunt Lucky was at the house with her magic jug and that if Two-Bits could have a swig of that miracle potion he might come around.

It took two men to hoist Two-Bits' head up high enough to pour a generous portion from the magic jug down the horse's gullet. As I say, I didn't know what Aunt Lucky had in that jug—and I don't know to this day—but I'm here to tell you that Two-Bits not only pricked up his ears within a half hour, but he won the big race of the afternoon.

Getting back to Aunt Lucky, it was the day of "kill or cure," and the doctor usually left a liberal supply of medicine with her to get the job done. I think she got the name "Lucky" because most of her patients lived; they were lucky, too.

And 'twas said that once in a great while when Aunt Lucky had a spell o' ailin' she would take a swig or two from the magic jug herself. Not all medicine makers will take their own concoctions. I don't know whether it cured her, but I do know that it did not kill her, at least not directly.

She lived to a ripe old age and built herself a monument. I doubt that anyone in that isolated community ever heard of Florence Nightingale. Very few could have told you that Carry Nation was an American temperance crusader who got into the newspapers by smashing saloon fixtures and supplies with a hatchet. But there was not a man, woman or child in that community who did not know who Aunt Lucky was. The monument she built was not of marble or granite, which eventually would weather away. Hers was a useful life that left a monument of memory, which grew in fact and fancy until she became one of the legendary characters of the community. A sort of Paul Bunyan of the carbuncle country.

Since then I have often thought of Aunt Lucky. What a figure she would have cut at an international medical congress or at a meeting of a learned medical society! If she were here today I would like to introduce her to my colleagues as a pioneer psychologist and psychiatrist.

I almost forgot to say she did die, at some ninety-odd

years. One night after a blizzard she saw a light at the hilltop home of a neighbor. That light, as late as 10 o'clock at night, was a beacon to her that someone was ill. Aunt Lucky grasped her jug and started out the door. It would be mere supposition to say that she took a snort from the jug to brace herself against the wintry blast. At any rate, she slipped on her ice-coated steps, broke her hip in two places and shattered the magic jug into a hundred pieces. They found her there the next morning. A couple of gnarled old fingers held the jug handle in a viselike death grip.

I don't know whether it was because Aunt Lucky had boosted me in the community or because of my own enterprise, or perhaps a combination of the two, but my practice grew. I was glad to have a partner; Dr. Goddard was a fine man. We were together almost twelve years in Holland. Our verbal agreement for the partnership was a fifty-fifty share in income. Actually we lived out of the same pocketbook. There was one bank account, one set of books.

He encouraged me in my surgical ambitions. I felt I had inadequate training along that line, and I knew I would have to study to keep up with developments. He stayed behind and took care of our practice while I went to Chicago for a summer course at the Chicago Post-Graduate College.

There, during the summer of 1900, I took advantage of every spare moment to improve myself.

At Holland I had been experimenting with a hypodermic sedative for use in obstetrical cases to relieve pain and the stress of labor. It was a combination of morphine, scopolamine and an alkaloid of digitalis. Those drugs were available in separate hypodermic tablets. I wanted a single tablet, easily soluble.

Some doctors at the college told me there was a doctor

out on Cottage Street who specialized in making hypodermic tablets. One Saturday afternoon I got on the Cottage Street car, and went out to his home. I was directed out to his cowbarn laboratory, where he was hard at work. You know, folks in Chicago had built back their cowbarns after Mrs. O'Leary's cow kicked over the lantern that started the great Chicago fire of 1871.

I mention this because the doctor, Wallace C. Abbott, was somewhat of a local historian, and he told me some tales of human heroism and of depravity and greed in the wake of the great fire. Dr. Abbott was a Vermont Yankee who had come to Chicago some years previously.

When we finally got around to talking about my Texas hypodermic problem he told me to come back the next Saturday and he would have a supply of the tablets ready. So he had, the next Saturday afternoon, but he told me he thought an alkaloid of cactus (cactus grandiflorus) would be better than digitalis. In fact he was thinking of using the cactus alkaloid in the commercial production of a sedative.

He told me he was going to organize a company capitalized at $10,000 for the manufacture of his product. He invited me to take out $1,000 in stock. I had a mind to do it, but I didn't, and that is probably where I let a few millions slip. Dr. Abbott organized the Abbott Alkaloidal Company, which later became the Abbott Laboratories. That was the beginning of the famous H.M.C. (hyoscine, morphine, cactine) tablet for pain and narcosis, which thousands of doctors use today.

I was about ready to return to Holland, but I went off sightseeing first, and it was then, I think, that this bonanza slipped my mind.

THE HURRICANE

My summer course completed, I wanted to see something of the Windy City and its environs.

On Sunday, September 9, 1900, I was a passenger on a whaleback excursion boat on Lake Michigan. That night the lake was most unusually rough. A nor'wester was blowing. The vessel rolled and pitched in the turbulent waves which at times swept over her decks. Several passengers were thrown out of their bunks and two of them suffered dislocated shoulders. I treated the injured passengers as I was the only one aboard who would admit to being a doctor.

As the sun rose the next morning we were approaching Chicago. Breakfast time came. All my life I have enjoyed breakfast, and it takes more than a storm at sea, or on land, to keep me from the breakfast table. The captain and I were the only ones who appeared in the dining room that morning.

The skipper said, "Something terrible has happened, perhaps far south of us; the capful of wind we had on the lake was nothing."

For a week there had been weather-bureau reports of a hurricane in the Caribbean Sea and the Gulf of Mexico, but no one paid much attention. The nor'wester we had on the lake was not part of the hurricane, and it has always been a mystery to me how the skipper knew a real storm had hit elsewhere. In those days the weather bureau did not use girls' names to designate hurricanes. This one should have been called Demonica.

When we landed I walked up Michigan Avenue. Newsboys were yelling, "Storm at Galveston, everybody killed or drowned!" I came to the building where the *Chicago American* was published. I decided to go in and find out all I could about the storm that had hit my home state. I headed for the newsroom four flights up.

The first person I came in contact with happened to be an aide—a secretary or something—to William Randolph Hearst. While we were talking, Mr. Hearst himself came along. The aide introduced me to him and told him I was a doctor from Texas. We talked about the Galveston storm situation. Mr. Hearst questioned me quickly and closely.

He wanted to do something, but Galveston was 1,300 miles and about forty hours away.

He invited me into his office.

Hearst owned a chain of newspapers, including two in California and one or two large dailies in New York as well as the *Chicago American*. He had just established the Chicago paper. Already he had become a controversial figure in politics and journalism, and was being discussed and cussed quite freely. Many regarded him as a hardheaded, selfish, arrogant person. The opposition cartoonists caricatured his face to look like a dollar mark. He was not credited with any large charity.

He asked me what railroads ran to Galveston and what I thought were the immediate needs of the stricken city. He inquired whether I could get doctors and nurses as a relief crew. I told him I would try. He called his secretary and asked me to give the secretary a list of things a relief train should have. He personally telephoned the Santa Fe railway office and asked for a fast train to be made ready. It was then 8:30 a.m. He ordered supplies aboard the train. Mr. Hearst wrote a check for $50,000, "incidental expenses," he called it, and told the secretary to have it cashed.

Then and there, I, who had shared the view that the newspaper magnate was self-centered, changed my mind. I saw one of the most unselfish acts I've ever known, even considering its publicity value. Thereafter, if anything mean was said about Mr. Hearst it did not register with me; in fact, I resented it.

He was about to do this for humanitarian reasons, and it did not take him long to make up his mind and get things started. Galveston was a long way out of his circulation area. On the front page he published an appeal for up to ten volunteer doctors, ten female nurses and four orderlies. They were to report to me at the Post-Graduate College. Cots, mattresses, blankets, portable sterilizers, portable operating tables and other equipment and supplies were rushed to the train.

From among those who volunteered I selected five doctors, eleven nurses and four chore boys. In addition, we had Mr. Hearst's manager and his secretary. I was director of medical activities. I've lost my list of that crew; I wish I had it; I wonder how many of them are living today. After the flood on the island there was a flood of books on the market about the disaster. In some of these accounts I was referred to as "Alkali Ike," which was a common nickname for a ruffian, and all Texans were supposed to be ruffians. In some of the books I was mentioned merely as "Dr. Crossway."

We had a Pullman car, a half-Pullman, a parlor car, a diner and two baggage cars.

I don't recall just how many hours it took us to reach Houston, about fifty miles from Galveston, but it was the fastest train ride I ever had taken.

It was about midnight when we arrived in Houston. We were met by one of Mr. Hearst's live-wire reporters, Mrs. Winifred Black, who had a nationwide reputation as a newspaperwoman. She had been unable to send news out of Galveston because all communications were down, and she had returned to Houston to send her dispatches.

She told us that estimates of the dead in Galveston ran all the way from 3,000 to 10,000 and that the latter figure probably was more nearly correct. She didn't know how the injured were being taken care of; two or three hospitals in Galveston were badly damaged. She told us that practically no buildings were undamaged, and she doubted that we would find a large building in condition to serve as a temporary hospital.

It was obvious that our job was going to be bigger than we had expected.

Hearst's manager peeled off a roll of $20 bills. There must have been several thousand dollars. He didn't count the money, nor did I. He told me to proceed to Galveston with the medical crew, to use the money for expenses, and, if I needed more, to let him know.

The terminus of the Santa Fe Railroad was Texas City, about six or eight miles across the bay from Galveston, I guess. An engine and a couple of flat cars had just arrived in Houston from Texas City. We made a deal with the engineer to make another trip. Some coffins had to be shipped down there anyway. So, within an hour after our arrival in Houston, we were enroute to Texas City, arriving there about three a. m. A full moon bathed the devastation.

There was not much left of Texas City. The track we pulled in on was a switch to a cotton compress. The concrete floor of the compress and a large iron safe, turned over, were all that remained of the plant.

Once since then, Texas City has suffered disaster. In 1947, explosions and fires, set off by a chemical blast aboard a ship in port, killed about 500 persons, injured about 5,000 and left property damage of $50,000,000.

Damage from the 1900 hurricane was less, proportionately, of course, but the survivors were stunned and shocked.

At the edge of the water there was a fellow sitting on a crate of caskets. He had some old-fashioned brown paper such as newspapermen used in those days. He said he represented one of Hearst's papers and that his name was Hawthorne.

"Not Nathaniel Hawthorne?" I said.

But he was in no mood for jokes. He said he had written storm stories, but had been unable to get them out of Texas City. I suggested that he send them to Mrs. Black by train and let her telegraph the stories from Houston.

After he got his stories off, he became more communicative.

"Over there," he said, pointing to a glow in the sky over the Galveston beachfront, "they're burning bodies by the hundreds. First they tried dumping the corpses in the gulf, but they kept coming back with the tide. Bloated bodies danced like corks on the waves. A few corpses have been picked up around here. And even caskets, long buried in Galveston cemeteries, have been dug up by the swirling flood and cast upon the water. Some of them have landed here."

Beached near the shore was a ship listing at about 30 degrees. We noticed a light or two on the ship. One of my orderlies, an ex-sailor, shouted, "Ship ahoy!"

A couple of men put out from the vessel. We made a deal whereby they were to use their rowboat to ferry our party across the bay to Galveston. This service was to cost us $20. The men told us their ship was the Kendall Castle, a British steamer. They told us a half-dozen oceangoing ships were beached or hard aground, and that scores of smaller boats were sunk or driven inland.

The rowboat made its way through the debris, sometimes shoving aside corpses. We began to wonder just what to expect in Galveston.

Galveston Island is about twenty-five miles long and seven miles at its greatest width.

The city, at that time with a population of about 40,000, was situated near the eastern end of the island where the land narrowed down to a width of a mile or two. On one side was the gulf, on the other the bay. The layout of the city was very simple. The streets that ran across the island from the gulf to the bay were numbered. Avenues, running the length of the island, were designated by letters of the alphabet.

Bridges across the bay, connected the city with the mainland.

Galveston was a resort and a port. Weekend excursions, with special reduced rates offered by the railroads, brought thousands of visitors, especially during the summer. The weekend before the storm one of the attractions for hinterlanders was a U. S. battleship anchored in the harbor. The port of Houston was not yet developed, and Galveston was a great cotton-shipping center, as well as an import point for finished goods from the east and abroad.

On the gulf, or south shore of the island, there was a fine beach twenty miles long. On Sunday afternoons family parties in surreys, wagons and "dago carts" drove along the sand packed hard by the tide.

Well-to-do residents of the city usually kept a stable of fine horses and a Jersey cow or two.

From all accounts, it began raining early Saturday morning, September 8. A norther (northwest wind) began banking water up on the north shore of the island. For several days the U. S. Weather Bureau had posted bulletins on the progress of a West Indian hurricane that had hit Jamaica, Cuba and Florida. For two weeks the disturbance had been dancing around in the Caribbean and the gulf while holidaymakers danced ashore. I was told that the gulls and sea birds had flown far inland, but man did not take heed. And the chill, driving rain from the north on Saturday morning was not alarming.

By afternoon, though, the norther had driven baywaters and rainfall far onto the north shore of the island. The wind shifted from northwest to northeast. It increased in intensity and when the weather bureau anemometer blew away at 5:17 p. m. the wind had reached a velocity of 100 miles an hour. It turned to the east and then the southeast, and gulf waters then began to engulf the south side of the island. It is estimated that the maximum velocity was from 110 to 120 miles per hour. It blew great guns and marline spikes all along the gulf coast, then spent its fury on the interior as far as three hundred miles. The wind let up on the island about midnight, and the waters receded before daylight. The water had been three feet deep on the highest ground of the island; and as much as ten feet deep elsewhere.

Meanwhile the island had been a seething maelstrom of death and destruction in darkness. All connections with the outside world—bridges, cables, telegraph, telephone—had been broken. Public utilities were crippled, if not destroyed. Gas and electricity were not available, and the street railway system was out, but some of the water mains, fortunately, were still in working order.

When we landed there we went to the Tremont Hotel where the water had receded, the slime and silt had been removed, and there were some rooms for our boys.

The hotel was on a high ridge of the island. We were told that water had been three or four feet deep in the lobby, but a great many lives had been saved because residents found refuge on upper floors of the hotel.

The town was under martial law. An adjutant deputized me as a deputy marshal and handed me a brace of pistols. I told him I was a doctor and didn't need guns, but he insisted that I go armed; that it was dangerous to go unarmed.

Later, when I saw soldiers shooting robbers, I knew what he meant.

When daylight came we got a better view of the devastation that had visited the island city the day I was on the storm-tossed excursion steamer on Lake Michigan.

You have seen meadows during the haying season. The farmer uses a dump rake to rake the hay into long windrows so that the bull rake can start at one end of the windrow and shove the whole thing together, ready to go into the baler.

About 1,500 acres facing the gulf, including about sixty blocks, had been raked by wind and wave. All of this wreckage had been deposited about a half mile from the beach, along about Avenue M. This wreckage, from about 30th Street to about 40th Street, formed a windrow ten to thirty feet high. In this windrow there were many of the victims, some living, many dead.

The first job of the survivors was to dig out the living, and then dispose of the dead.

Summerlike temperatures followed the storm, and the stench of the dead made it nauseating for the rescue squads.

And in the removal of the corpses, which was in progress when we arrived, sometimes it was necessary for the military to press workers into service and then stand guard while the job was done. The "dead gangs" covered their nostrils with bandana handkerchiefs, saturated with disinfectant, to make their work tolerable.

To begin with, more than two thousand bodies were carted to the water front, placed aboard barges and taken out into the gulf where they were dumped after being weighted down with stones and chunks of concrete. But it was a hurry-up job and, anyway, many of the bodies were in such a state of decomposition that the weights were not secure. The bodies bobbed to the surface and came to the beach on the incoming tide.

Then we organized burial squads. Their job was to bury on the beach, or burn if possible, the bodies that came back from the gulf. But, as I have said, the beach area was swept clean, and there was little fuel for cremation. So, some of the bodies were buried in the soggy earth. That is the reason, to this very day, why excavators for construction projects on the Galveston water front sometimes run into human bones.

In the windrow area it was a simpler matter. The workmen could take wood from the windrow, form a funeral pyre and place the bodies on it. It might have been even simpler to set the windrow itself on fire, but, after the many miraculous escapes we heard of, it was not beyond imagination that there still were living beings in that long line of debris. The proposal to burn the windrow also was opposed on the grounds that every bit of lumber that could be salvaged would be needed in reconstruction.

There were those who had religious scruples against disposing of their dead by fire, but no one knew who was who.

Uninjured survivors who found the bodies of their lost ones on their premises were thankful. They could bury them there, evading the disposal squads policing the area under military guard.

One of the largest hospitals, St. Mary's, consisted of a main building of sturdy brick construction, and a cluster of wooden barracklike structures. The main building was damaged, and the wooden structures were swept away. A young medical student was credited with saving scores of patients from the barracks. He fought his way through the raging storm and transferred the patients, one by one, to the main building.

The union depot, which remained intact, we were told, had sheltered many residents through the storm.

The Catholic Orphanage was destroyed and we were told that about one hundred children and nuns lost their lives. Apparently some of the sisters had tried to save their charges by tying ropes around their middles and then securing the ropes to themselves. Several groups were found thus tethered in death.

An undetermined number died in the Old Women's Home.

Hundreds perished when the Rosenberg School, at Avenue H and 11th Street, was pounded into wreckage. Many residents had taken refuge in the school building soon after the storm hit.

The bodies of smaller groups and of individual victims were found scattered about. In many cases only corsets and shoes remained on the victims. Bloated corpses of horses, cows, mules, hogs and poultry were here and there; also dogs, cats and rats. Flies buzzed all over the place. The buzzard was almost a sacred bird in Texas because of his scavenger habits, but for some reason there wasn't a vulture in the sky over the island.

There was no one to count the dead and few to help the injured. Official estimates of the dead at that time were around 3,000; some newspapers placed the toll at 5,000. Many thousands were injured. Some 4,000 buildings were wrecked and property damage ran into many millions.

Later estimates of the dead, including an estimate attributed to Texas' Governor Joe Sayers, were as high as 12,000, but the toll probably never will be known.

There was not a frame building left intact. At the medical department building of the University of Texas wreckage was piled up around it up to the third floor. We selected the Ball High School at Avenue H and 22nd as an operating base. Wreckage was piled up around there, too, and the structure was damaged, but at least the building was tenable. The next day we brought our supplies to the high school building and opened a relief station. The injuries were mostly broken limbs and lacerations, some cases of exposure, but there were others who were beyond human help.

A lawless element turned up to prey on the dead. Robbers—men and women, white and black—took finger rings, earrings, stickpins and money belts off the victims. In some cases swollen fingers and ears were cut off to get the jewelry. Vampires who were caught with such grisly evidence in their possession were shot. I recall one case, a preacher's son from upstate who tried to run with his loot when he was ordered to halt, and he was shot down.

Most of the looters were individuals or gangs who had come in there in the wake of the storm. Many of them were harpies and ne'er-do-wells. I suppose in their warped minds they justified their acts by the thought that the jewelry was a loss anyway when the bodies were cast in the sea or on a pyre, and that it was a legitimate windfall for them.

We set up a salvage station where jewelry and other valuables were turned in. I saw the bodies of a couple brought in, lashed together. Secured to the woman's corset was a roll of currency as big as a gallon bucket.

A few mornings after our arrival I was eating breakfast at the Tremont Hotel. A man, about fifty, came in. He was a Virginian, but had made his home on Avenue I in Galveston. He said he had just come in from a trip East. I knew there was nothing left on Avenue I, but I didn't want to be the one to tell him. He had left his wife, five children and his mother-in-law there. We went out to where they were supposed to live. We found Avenue I all right; the Army had put up temporary street markers.

There was an old Negro sitting on what was left of the concrete steps of the Virginian's mansion. Apparently asleep, he held his head cupped in his hands. At the sound of our approach over the rubble-strewn street he roused up.

"Lawd, Boss, dey's all gone," he said.

"Where?" asked the Virginian.

The Negro pointed to a cleared spot in the garden. The family had been buried there.

"Boss, I knowed you'd come," he said. "I come back here

after de storm an' buried 'em. I wanted to make coffins, but there warn't enough wood left o' de house.

"Boss, you remembers dat table in de livin' room, de table wid a top made o' genuwine Eyetalian marble. Missus always tole me to be extra careful dustin' dat table. Dat table wuz de only thing left o' the furniture, an' it was busted up. I took de biggest piece o' marble I could find an' used it fur a tombstone for Missus. You can see it yonder, Boss.

"There warn't nothin' much left to mark de others. I took a piece of Miss Virginia's plaid skirt an' tied it to a stick to mark hers. She liked dat dress so much. I took pieces o' clothes to mark de rest o' them."

The only other memento the Virginian could find was a fragment of his wife's hand-painted china.

After we got straightened out a bit and a temporary bridge was put up we drove out of Galveston with a team and wagon loaded with groceries and medical supplies, and a nurse. For five or six miles we saw all kinds of furniture and pianos scattered about.

On a subsequent trip to the same area, three days later, I noticed that all of the pianos and most of the furniture were gone. I asked one of the residents what had happened. He said folks from the interior had come down and carted the stuff away. Some of the owners were helpless, perhaps maimed, but the intruders offered no help.

There was a passenger train that had rolled over two or three times. The passengers who drowned were divested of their valuables.

Disaster often brings out the worst—and the best—in humanity.

I mention the worst because it seemed odd under the circumstances. The other part of the story has never been told adequately. Darkness that night hid many acts of heroism. Only a few came to pillage, many came to succor. Ours was only one of a number of rescue and relief teams.

Some of the low-built houses in the outlying area remained standing, though. In one house we found an old man with his leg broken; his wife with a bruised arm. A ten-year-old grandchild, whose parents had been lost in the storm, was trying to take care of them. We loaded them in the wagon, and by the time we got back to town we had a wagonload of similar cases. For others we left groceries.

For still others, visitors in the city who were stranded, we bought tickets back to their home towns.

We made generous use of whatever disinfectants were at hand, quicklime, chloride of lime, carbolic acid. The pestilence which we had feared in the wake of the storm did not materialize. Possibly one reason was because the water supply was not contaminated; it came from artesian wells on the mainland.

There had been some friction between civil and military authorities in Galveston during the twelve days of martial law, but many reports of these things were exaggerated.

In fact, the whole storm story was pretty badly garbled and before I finish my say on this episode in my career I want to correct some misconceptions.

They say there was a tidal wave in the wake of the hurricane. A tidal wave comes and goes quickly. It might have meant quicker and easier death in Galveston. This was what some weather men preferred to call a storm wave, a great mass of ocean water driven ashore by a hurricane, and it kept piling up during the six hours that the storm was at its height. Frame houses collapsed, and the elements used the debris as battering rams against sturdier construction. There was time for long periods of terror, which frequently is not the case in tidal waves.

I have mentioned some summary executions for looting. I believe the accounts of the number of persons killed have been grossly exaggerated. I have seen published reports that the U. S. Army and the Texas National Guard "shot over one hundred ghouls." I did not see everything that went on in Galveston's darkest hour, but I venture to say there were only a half dozen executions. But they were carried out so promptly and so publicly that they served as an effective deterrent to further looting and desecration of the dead.

Another libel that was published was that many of the survivors were raving maniacs. It is true that there were a few cases of temporary mental derangement, possibly due to bereavement or some harrowing experience in the storm. But these were few, indeed, compared with the many who lived through the storm in fortitude and mental stability.

There were reports that the hair of young men turned gray overnight. I didn't examine them before and after, but I've never seen anything like that happen to anyone in distress. It must be a figure of speech.

Still another report I would like to correct was that relief expeditions such as ours, and many others, hampered reconstruction because the residents, provided for by outsiders, refused to work. There were unpleasant jobs such as those of the "dead gangs," where a show of arms sometimes was necessary, but generally the surviving populace turned to with a will.

It was published that the wharves were all gone. Actually the first contact with the outside world after the storm was by tugs that tied up at the wharves. The first news of the extent of disaster was carried out by boat. The first refugees left by ship and some of the first relief came in by water.

Galveston was suffering for want of water and food, according to first accounts. I have stated that some of the water mains were intact. Also, some cisterns, filled brimful by the rainfall that preceded the real blow, withstood the wind. Not all the merchandise in stores was ruined, and some merchants sold at wholesale prices, or gave away food that was likely to spoil anyway. Much of the grain in some of the damaged elevators was in good condition. It was the beginning of the oyster season, and oyster luggers which had run for cover before the storm or were cast ashore yielded food for a day or two. Fishing schooners, too, were beached, or in some cases driven far inland. Such cargoes were a blessing for a day or two until they became a nuisance in adding to the stench of putrefaction.

There was also the report that Galveston would not rebuild on the island, that the wrecked city was to be abandoned, and perhaps re-establish itself on the mainland. This rumor was soon spiked, and, of course, the beautiful island city today, with its seawall and its oleanders and its palms, is living evidence that no thought of abandonment was entertained very long.

Strangely enough, in all this sensationalism, the actual death toll dwarfed the wildest figment of the imagination. First reports were that there were 1,000 dead; then perhaps 2,500; then 5,000, then 7,000, and finally almost a week after the storm, the official figure of 12,000 admittedly might have been an underestimation.

Because means of communication were crippled, the wildest rumors gained currency on the island. Many of these rumors were fed to the outside world as gospel. If we ever have an atomic catastrophe—which God forbid—the first objective should be to re-establish communications. The lack of news nourishes demoralization and despair.

We closed out our activities there and moved to Houston, where we opened up in the City Auditorium. We transferred all our patients and equipment from Galveston to Houston. That took a day and a night. Some of our personnel was released and I was left in charge. One by one we evacuated our patients. The time was approaching for us to fold our tents and silently steal away. I handed Mr. Hearst's manager what was left of the roll of bills he had given me—without counting the money. I never knew how much I had spent, but it must have been several thousand dollars. Nor did he count what was left. He peeled off several bills, handed them to me and said, "I guess this will get you back to your home town."

And I landed back in Holland with ten dollars left over from the Hearst funds.

The strange thing about the whole proceeding was the lack of bookkeeping. No questions asked, no receipts, but an emergency situation had been met. It was a reminder that confidence in individual integrity is repaid in honesty.

Obviously the medical supplies and facilities at our disposal in hurricane relief work were modest compared with those of today. They were modest even compared with those of World War I in which I served as a neurosurgeon, and they were primitive when you consider what we had to work with in the Waco tornado of 1953.

MUD, MARRIAGE AND MALARIA

WHEN I got back to Holland after the Galveston storm, I found the community almost prostrate with malaria. Swarms of mosquitoes had been blown into the interior from the coastal region. These insects included the malaria-bearing anopheles.

It kept raining, and nowhere in the world can it get muddier than in that fertile blackland belt. It seemed to me that mud and malaria were conspiring to undo me and the community. My ally was the horse.

I've read a lot about doctors on horseback and about horse-and-buggy doctors, but I don't recall that anyone has ever given the horse due credit. Some colts are just born to be doctors' horses. A good horse has about as much sense as a doctor. A well-trained doctor's horse senses an emergency. He pricks up his ears and is alert. And he knows when the emergency is over. Going home he just droops his head and jogs along. That is not true of all horses. As you know, many farm animals are sluggish when they start out on a job in the field, but hell-for-leather when they head for home.

During that rainy fall the roads stayed muddy, and there were few bridges. Frequently my horse and I had to ford or swim swollen creeks. I would hoist the saddlebags to keep them dry; they were my drugstore and medical kit.

When the roads were not too boggy and the streams were not too flooded, I used a buggy and horse. In the black-land belt, where during rainy weather the wheels sank to the hubs into the mire, it frequently was necessary to hitch two horses to the buggy.

Rubber-tired buggies came in after a while, and it looked like we were headed for the millennium at a pretty fast clip. The old ladies clucked their tongues and declared we were bound straight for perdition. I am sure there was some courting and sparking done in those rubber-tired buggies.

The operating base for a lot of this horse-drawn society was the livery stable. I have talked about the old wagon yards in Mississippi where, in the '90s, you could park your wagon and sleep yourself and your team. The livery stable could be considered the successor to the old wagon yard. You could hire a mount or horse and buggy at the livery stable, or you could leave your own there while you went on about your business. And if you were hard up for a place to stay overnight a bale of hay spread out in the livery stable was not too uncomfortable.

Progress sometimes results in inconveniences. It seemed to me that farmers went hog-wild with barbed wire. Fencing land meant there had to be gates. Many of these gates consisted merely of three strands of wire tied to a sapling. Such gates were called gaps.

Around and through a section of land, 640 acres, you could expect to find several gates or gaps. It got to where the small towns themselves were almost fenced in. This was because farmers all around town were fencing their properties. In Holland there was only one road leading out of town where one did not have to open a gate of some kind.

This made it hard on the doctor or anyone else having to travel a long distance horseback or in a buggy. One had to dismount from his horse or get out of the buggy, open the gate, drive through, and then close the gate again. To leave a gate open, where a man's livestock could stray, was a dastardly deed; almost as bad as stealing a horse. Straying livestock could play havoc with a cornfield.

I remember once being called to the home of an old settler there. The late Ernest W. Spiegelhauer lived about four miles from Holland. Some member of the family was ill.

Whoever was sent to town to tell me to come out had left a gate open. When I rode up the gate was wide open and the Spiegelhauer horses were trampling down the corn.

There was no one else outside except the old man, and he was pretty excited. He was a fine old Texas German who never quite mastered the English language.

When I inquired what all the excitement was about he said, "Some damn fool shut the gate wide open, turned the horses inside out, and where in the hell is nobody?"

I got awfully tired of opening and closing gates. It must have been an inspiration; it struck me that the sensible thing to do was to have someone ride with me and drive through the gates while I held them open.

Maybe, if Roberta would consent to become my wife, she could drive through the gateways while I held open the gates. You will remember she was my brightest pupil when I taught school in Holland.

When I returned from medical school I often found her nursing and helping out with my patients. We began to have dates as often as I could get one; she was very popular and had many admirers. Her aunt permitted her to go with me on some of my calls. Our excuse was that she would help out with the nursing or sit up with the patient, a common practice in those days. Not all of our conversation was strictly medical. Thus a real romance began.

Another doctor sold me his cottage and I fixed it up with office and bachelor quarters. That arrangement did not last very long. We got married at high noon, November 25, 1900.

Her friends told Roberta she would starve to death if she married that young doctor. She told them we would starve together.

However, things looked rosy that day. It was a simple Bible wedding by a Baptist preacher, sans music, presents, attendants. We sat down to a turkey dinner.

Just as dinner was over I had an emergency call to see a patient who was a tubercular. He was having a hemorrhage. My bride went with me. While I was busy trying to relieve my patient, who had bled white, she was applying heat pads to his feet and body. She made a bigger hit with the patient and his family than I did. They called her "Mrs. Doctor," and ever thereafter she was known in that community, and wherever we went, as Mrs. Doctor.

That was the first of many hundreds of calls that Mrs. Doctor made with me. No man was ever so blessed. She was my helpmeet, advisor and companion. Some day, she said, I would write a book of my experiences as a doctor.

We made a trip to Temple, some twenty miles north of Holland. Temple must have had a population of three or four thousand, and it was said that the town stretched for two miles. That was quite a metropolitan expanse in horse-and-buggy days. My bride bought our furniture and furnishings there.

It was the next year before we made a honeymoon journey, and then it was combined with business. Dr. Goddard, ever willing, would take care of my patients.

Just to show you some of the quirks of fate, this honeymoon trip came about in this manner:

In those days there was quite a vogue of guessing the number of beans in a glass jar, and the individual who guessed nearest the correct number usually received a handsome prize. I suppose it was the 1901 edition of our present give-away program.

Anyway, a tenant-farmer patient of mine won the local bean-guessing contest, and the prize was two round-trip railroad tickets, Pullman and meals, to New York City, and three days at the plush Hotel Belleclaire.

Now, that tenant farmer had no more use for those tickets than I would have today for round-trip tickets to the moon. So he and I were not long in coming to terms. I don't recall now just how we traded; it might have been that I took out his appendix or his wife's tumor. I just don't recall. At any rate, there was no cash involved and both of us were satisfied.

At least I was; I was off on my honeymoon at last. The big city where, in my boyhood, I had dreamed of practicing, was within my reach, at least for a few days. For a Mississippi-bred country boy from Texas the prospect of seeing the wonders of New York was a stroke of good fortune, indeed, all done with a bunch of beans in a glass jar. Once there, I marveled at the subway under construction at City Hall and I gawked at the twenty-story Flatiron Building, which was nearing completion.

And the first thing I knew I was doing surgery in New York, too. The way that came about was a bit unusual.

I had heard of Dr. John A. Wyeth, founder of the New

York Polyclinic and Hospital, the first of its kind in this country. Dr. Wyeth was not only a physician and surgeon, but a soldier, financier, statesman, writer and orator. During the War Between the States he had served in the Alabama cavalry and for sixteen months was a prisoner of the Yankees.

I wanted to meet this celebrated Southerner. I sought out his modestly furnished office. While I was waiting to see him a man came in holding his hand over his groin. Dr. Wyeth eyed him as he motioned him to a straight-backed chair and said, "My good man, how long have you had that rupture?" The man said, "Ten years."

"Then how long has it been down so that you could not get it back?"

"Since last night."

"You go on over to the hospital," said the doctor. "We will operate right away."

The patient had an inguinal hernia, complete and strangulated.

Dr. Wyeth had made no examination before sending the man to the hospital. I was impressed by his powers of perception and observation. I wanted to be more like this great surgeon.

I lost no time in enrolling as a student in the polyclinic for the summer. Dr. Wyeth's assistant was a Dr. Bodine, whose first name or initials I do not recall. I was invited to assist them in their surgery. I helped Dr. Bodine do a hernia under local anesthetic up on Fifth Avenue. For several operations we had to journey to Blackwells Island (Welfare Island).

One night we had a difficult tumor case on the island, and there was some delay. After the operation was over, we discovered that the ferry had tied up for the night, and it looked as if we were stuck until daylight. But there was an all-night saloon open and a lot of politicians were having a powwow. They invited us in, and a special boat came after the party about three a. m. By that time my bride had the whole metropolitan police looking for me. She was considerably upset, and I don't think she ever quite believed my story.

But she got revenge. The bean-jar scrip, of course, had played out and we had moved from the swank hotel at Broadway and 77th to a boardinghouse on 34th near Fifth Avenue. One day while I was busy at the hospital Mrs. Crosthwait decided to go shopping downtown. Coming back she got on the "L," but when the train got to 34th St. it did not stop long enough for her to get off, so she rode on out to the end of the line. Must have been the Bronx. By the time she started back the evening traffic was so heavy again that she missed getting off the train at 34th and wound up 'way downtown. She hailed a hansom and finally got home. I was waiting. When she came in she said, "No questions, no argument, we are even now."

Speaking of arguments, I was witness in New York to a controversy that illustrated the fact that surgical practices still had a long way to go.

A member of Dr. Wyeth's staff operated on about one major case a day and he usually had an average of about one death a day and an autopsy every night. He was a great believer in autopsies. It was part of my course to observe autopsies.

This doctor used his bare hands in autopsies and the following morning he used his bare hands in surgery.

Dr. Wyeth demanded that the doctor use rubber gloves

in his surgery. Both doctors were a bit stubborn. The offending doctor flatly refused to use rubber gloves.

The issue—rubber gloves vs. bare hands—developed into bitterness, the staff became divided and the medical profession took sides.

Some city politics crept into the controversy. The charity patients, who constituted the majority of the cases, were under the city's supervision. That was the day of the pamphleteer. The surgeon who refused to don the gloves wrote a pamphlet the title of which, as well as I can recall it, was "The Hand of Wood in a Glove of Steel." He claimed that the operating surgeon's tactile sensation was lost or greatly impaired by use of rubber gloves; that rubber gloves caused bunglesome and prolonged surgery, and that they contributed to infections rather than prevented them.

The New York Academy of Medicine was the ruling medical society of New York. The organization called a special meeting to discuss the question whether a surgeon should be required to wear rubber gloves in his surgical work after doing autopsies with his bare hands. Dr. Wyeth invited me to the meeting. I would estimate that there were about four hundred persons present, and apparently each one wanted to have his say in the great debate. I cannot recall that I ever attended a meeting of any kind where there was more argument and less reason or logic. The night meeting lasted until two a. m. Without going into all the pros and cons it may be said that finally they adopted a motion that no surgeon should be allowed to operate with bare hands on any city or charity patient within seven days after he had performed an autopsy.

This incident in the big city struck me as rather strange because I had been using rubber gloves even in remote

Texas. I have the impression now that at that time the question whether a surgeon used rubber gloves or not depended a whole lot on where he got his medical training. Some institutions insisted upon the use of gloves; others didn't. It all hinged on your old college tie.

But all good things come to an end, and so did the summer's course at the polyclinic. In addition to the bean-jar prize, we had spent my first year's earnings from my practice, but it was worth it. So we went back to Holland.

As I have said, malaria was prevalent in Texas, and I knew something about the disease because back in Mississippi I had grown up in a malarial atmosphere. They called it the ague. At that time malaria was thought to be wind-borne. Quinine was the only known remedy.

About two centuries previously the Countess of Chinchon, wife of the Viceroy of Peru, was cured of a fever, thought to have been malaria. The story was that she was cured by a remedy from the bark of a tree which came to be known as the Cinchona. That is the tree from which quinine is obtained. Several modern writers have declared that the story of the countess' powder was purely legendary. Be that as it may, the story served to establish the use of quinine in the treatment of malaria.

My mother used to give it to me by the handfuls in black coffee sweetened with brown sugar. Apparently it did not hurt me, but several of our neighbors died with what was called blackwater fever (falciparum malaria). All of them had taken large doses of quinine, especially on days when the congestive chill was due.

In Texas, too, I found the death rate rather high and quinine was being stoked into patients the way a fireman stokes coal into a firebox.

Patients would start out with a chill and high fever; the next day, a light chill in the forenoon and a hard one in the afternoon, and on the third day, an all-day chill. This was called a congestive chill. After several rounds of this, along with lots of quinine and calomel, came the dark, or bloody urine, and then the funeral.

In my first consultation with an old family doctor who had spent forty years in a malarial district I was told that the fatal cases of blackwater fever all had taken large doses of quinine. I pondered that statement and decided to abandon the use of quinine as soon as the first signs of dark or bloody urine appeared in my malarial patients.

Once, when I was called in consultation with another country doctor, I asked him what he had given the patient.

"Well," he replied, "the first thing I did I slugged him with a big dose of calomel and blue mass (purgative). Then I flushed him out with salts, and then poked the quinine to him in ten-grain doses."

By that time the patient was too ill to take anything more by mouth and that was a long time before intravenous medication. So we left him in the hands of the family and the Lord. He got well.

My wife's Uncle Cal gave me a fine microscope, along with the stains in use at that time. I began to examine specimens of dark, or bloody, urine.

Hemoglobin is the coloring matter in the red blood cells. When the red cells lose their hemoglobin in a destructive process known as hemolysis they become pale. They stain differently, they are easily identified and can be distinguished from hemoglobin itself.

The general belief around 1900 was that the reddish or dark-colored urine in malaria was due to blood, or whole red cells, in the urine. My theory was that it was hemoglobin which had been released by the disintegration of the red cells; that the hemoglobin was free in the extracellular fluid, and was thrown off through the kidneys.

So, too much quinine at the wrong time, became Suspect Number One.

I began to look for a substitute. Most of the concoctions made from barks and herbs were useless. There were certain nostrums sold in drugstores and many grocery stores. There was one called Grove's Chill Tonic. I suppose I took fifty bottles of it during the ten years I had chills and fever in Mississippi. It contained quinine. That ruled it out for patients who already had too much quinine in their systems. Then there was Warburg's Tincture. It proved unsuitable. I talked the matter over with an old doctor and an old pharmacist and we finally decided to try one of the sodium salts. We chose sodium biphosphate.

I realize this kind of treatment sounds rather primitive today, but that was fifty-five years ago.

A study of specimens of urine from quinine takers had shown a reaction strongly alkaline whereas the normal reaction is acid. The sodium salt selected was supposed to acidify the urine, and it did. Given in larger doses it acted as a diuretic and laxative. In sixty-grain doses it was a purgative.

There were various theories about what caused malaria, and a lot of superstition and folklore. For instance, there was some clearing of timberland going on. More farmers had come into the central Texas cattle country and there was considerable brush cutting to bring the land under cultivation. In the pine forests of east Texas there was lumbering to meet the demands for building materials.

Left over from these operations was a lot of waste wood, which was just piled up and allowed to rot. There was a popular idea that this decaying matter discharged a putrefactive vapor which, wafted by the wind, entered the human body and caused ague. It seemed to be worse during the winter rainy season.

That winter I did very well in my practice, thanks largely to malaria.

But sometimes the ironies of fate seem to strike unkind blows.

One day I received a wire from a doctor in my old home town, Houston, Mississippi, that my father was seriously ill with blackwater fever. I wired back to discontinue the use of quinine, and recommended maximum doses of sodium biphosphate. I caught the next train for Okolona. In those days it was a journey of two and a half days by rail. Then there were thirty miles to go by road. I hired a livery-stable horse and started for my father's place, my boyhood home. About five miles from Houston I met the doctor, who evidently was on a hurry-up call. He reined up just long enough to say, "Willie, your father is dead!" I rode on home. My father was in his casket; my mother was ill with malaria fever.

My telegram had been received but ignored. The old doctor was quoted as saying, "What does he know about malaria? I was treating blackwater fever before he was born."

He was right about that, but all along he had been doing the wrong thing at the wrong time, and country cemeteries bore doleful evidence of the inadequacies of the treatment of that time. The old doctor was doing just what all his contemporaries had been doing for years.

But I have never gotten over the untimely death of my father and the stab to my pride. He was fifty-four. I felt so keenly the loss, and the insult to my intelligence, that I spent all of my spare time in the study of malaria. Two years later I read a paper before the Texas State Medical Association on management of falciparum malaria. The paper was reproduced in several foreign journals and I received requests from abroad for copies of it.

What I said then no doubt is long outdated, but the point is that I thought I was making progress in my chosen profession.

I got tangled up in the newspaper business again. I should have known better. Remember that time when my editor got shot in Okolona, Mississippi; then there was the occasion when the Louisville newsboy made a monkey out of me.

My Holland newspapering came about this way:

There was a little weekly called the *Holland Progress*. The editor's wife had to have an operation, and I did the job. In those days weekly editors, who also were the publishers as a rule, would accept farm produce such as chickens, eggs or potatoes in lieu of cash subscriptions. I guess the editor figured if the barter system was good enough for editors it was good enough for doctors. So, instead of paying me cash for the treatment and surgery, he just gave me the *Progress*. For a few months I became editor-publisher as well as doctor.

This combination did not work out very well. I knew a lot of community news, but I couldn't print it. Perhaps I was a little outspoken in my editorial policy, too. At any rate, I decided to sell. The purchaser had only $50 cash, but he gave me a 150-year paid-up subscription as well as the cash. I've been receiving the paper ever since, fifty-four years, and my subscription is paid for another ninety-six years.

I lost money on that deal, but it was just as well. If I had kept the newspaper I probably would have got involved in lawsuits. There was only one lawyer in town. He was shrewd and clever, but not too reliable.

His shingle read, "Roddy I. Hoosier, the Ram Rod, Threatening to Practice Law." He was a retainer, or lawyer, for all of the three saloons in town. Usually he drank up his retainer fees far in advance.

Ram Rod was not too obnoxious even when he was in his cups. However, the local citizenry gradually lost patience with him. They could not get their legal business attended to unless they got to Ram Rod early in the morning before he started communing with John Barleycorn. The only other lawyer was at the county seat, twenty miles away, and that meant a day's journey. So Ram Rod had things pretty much his own way.

But finally Ram Rod's way of life came to be threatened. An old-timer there decided he would run for justice of the peace. The candidate promised the people that if he was elected he would sober up old Ram Rod even if he had to keep him in the calaboose until the town went dry. Under local option in vogue at the time each community or town or country could decide for itself whether liquor was to be prohibited or not.

Well, the candidate who had promised to sober up the town lawyer was elected justice of the peace. True to his word, he had the constable swear out a warrant against the lawyer for being drunk and making himself a general nuisance about town. Ram Rod was arrested and brought to trial. A large crowd was on hand to see the show.

Ram Rod maintained a dingy office in "the bat cave," a dilapidated old building. I doubt there was a law book in the place. Anyway he told the constable he had to have his law book, and the constable escorted him to the office, thence to the courtroom. Ram Rod appeared as his own attorney. 'Tis said that a man who serves as his own counsel has a fool for a client, but not so with Ram Rod.

He pleaded innocent on account of former jeopardy. He opened the large book, waved it before the honorable court and said, in his most sonorous tones, "If your honor please, this book says right here that a man cannot be put in jeopardy of life or liberty twice for the same offense."

The judge had no legal advisor, no prosecutor who might have challenged the defendant.

"If your honor please," continued Ram Rod, dropping the heavy tome in the seat of his chair, "the records of this town ought to show that a long time ago I paid a fine and spent a whole hour in jail, hot and thirsty, and, sir, I have not been sober since."

The court records, if there were any, were not consulted.

Ram Rod had some of his friends primed to come to his defense. They told the judge that the lawyer was right. Several of them remembered that he had paid a fine and had been locked up for drunkenness, and there were those who were willing to testify that Ram Rod had not drawn a sober breath since then.

I could go on like this, telling about characters around Holland. There seemed to be a lot of them there. The practice of the old-time country doctor brought him in close contact with the people. While he was delivering a baby his wife might be preparing breakfast for the infant's family. Sometimes it was not a question of prescribing medicine at all; there were occasions when talk was the best medicine. In many cases it was not just a doctor-patient connection, but a social relationship. I visited in my patients' homes whether they were ill or not and they came to see me whether they needed me or not. And that sort of thing goes on to this day to some extent although a modern clinic is hardly the setting for social intercourse.

I was beginning to build up a bit of a reputation in the community. When a doctor does that—and most anyone gains a following if he is conscientious—he is bound to be the target of individuals who might be as well off if they didn't have a doctor. No doctor likes to be bothered with this type when he knows there are others who need his services.

Generally I would divide these pests into two classes, those who have whims and those who have whines.

I don't mean to make light of real and genuine pain. What I am talking about is the person whose imagination runs away with him or he feigns illness.

The whimsical patient is spotted on his first visit. The dialogue runs something like this:

Doctor: You are Mrs. or Mr. So-and-So?

Patient: I certainly am.

Dr: What is your problem?

P: What do you mean?

Dr: I mean what is your illness, what ails you?

P: Ah, ha, that's for you to find out; that's what I came here for.

The whiners are just the opposite. They list every ailment in the book, and, if given time, they follow up with a new list at the next appointment.

There was an old couple who lived on a ranch a few miles from town. She was the whining kind. One cold night she wanted her husband to call the doctor; she thought she was going to die. The doctor went out and examined her and told her there was nothing wrong with her. The husband said, "I told you so." She ordered both the husband and the doctor out of her room and said, "Don't you ever come back."

The couple lived on for twenty years, but never spoke to each other directly. They had one of those old-fashioned double houses; that is, there were two sections with a breezeway hall in between. They lived there separately and communicated with each other by note or through the hired help or the children. The husband was the whimsical type; otherwise he would have found a way to soften her up and resume normal marital relations.

Another night there came the familiar "Hello!" at my front gate. A fifteen-year-old boy, mounted on a work mule, said "Doctor, you are wanted at once."

"What's the trouble?"

"Mr. Beerman's wife is dying. I am the neighbor's boy. My mammy is over there and she said for you to come quick."

I saddled up my pony and loped out there.

I got there just before the husband arrived; he had been in town all day and was pretty well loaded with his favorite beverage. He viewed the situation in silence. His wife was flat on the bed with four neighbor women rubbing her hands and feet. Her jaws were locked, lips closed tight and eyes shut, but her breathing and pulse were normal. She had been that way since noon. That was about the time she had expected her husband to return from town.

I looked the situation over and decided she was "throwing a hissy" for the benefit of the neighbors and to punish her husband.

So I said, in a loud voice, "She's in bad shape, liable to die any minute." (Moans and groans from the other women.) "But I have a remedy here that either will finish her off or bring her to; more often it kills."

I called for some hot water. I began to prepare a sterile water hypo and got her arm ready for the injection. She jerked the other arm free, slapped the hypodermic needle out of my hand, and jumped up yelling, "Get out of here, all of you!" That meant me, too. She spied her husband cowering over in one corner of the room, and she bolted into the kitchen after a skillet, a rolling pin or some other weapon. We didn't wait to see. The husband was right on my heels going out. After he got a safe distance he said to me, "Damn that woman, I'll fix her."

I don't know what he ever did, if anything, but I was glad to get out, and I was never called out there again.

There were quite a few cases like that, women throwing hissies. Frequently I would have the druggist fix up the worst, nastiest, stinkingest solution possible—tincture ammoniated valerian, asafoetida and garlic, all in one. The directions were one teaspoonful as needed. Usually one dose was more than enough.

CUTTIN' AN' SHOOTIN'

ALL KINDS of ailments, real and imaginary, contributed to my income as a general practitioner at a time when I was in need of finances. In addition, there were cuttings and shootings.

These days we don't seem to have much man-to-man combat. Maybe we are preoccupied looking at television or manufacturing bombs for mass extermination.

I wouldn't say that man was more courageous in the old days, but he seemed more prone to settle differences by hand-to-hand combat. In those days if you called a man a so-and-so or if you mentioned a lady's name while you were in a saloon you had a fight on your hands. A saloon was a drinking place for men only, and a lady's name was not to be uttered in the place, let alone letting one in. The weapons ranged all the way from bare fists to baseball bats, dirks and six-shooters.

I have indicated that at that time Holland had the reputation of being a "tough little burg," and some of the residents in the surrounding area were no less ornery. We were not too far from a Texas village called Cut-and-Shoot, and it was only two hours' horseback ride to Who'd-A-Thought-It.

One night I was called to the Who'd-A-Thought-It community. It was raining and the creeks were up. There was a lot of lightning and thunder. To while away the time I found myself repeating that old nursery rime, "The thunder rolled, the clouds looked big; the lightning flashed and killed my pig." But the flashes of lightning were welcome because they gave me an occasional glimpse of the road.

I found my patient to be a handsome young man, who was a house painter and paperer. He was a bachelor and he had been boarding with a couple while he was working on their house. Maybe a triangle developed, I don't know, but someone had severed one of the external jugular veins and when I got there he had just about bled himself bloodless. He didn't seem to want to live. He was too weak to place on the kitchen table, so I worked on him on the floor. I tied off the vein and sewed up the cut. After I had bandaged him up and the housewife had given him some strong coffee, we put a woman's nightgown on him and lifted him into bed.

By that time it was one or two o'clock in the morning, and it was pitch dark except for occasional flashes of lightning. I decided to stay until daylight. I lay down on a cot in the same room with my patient. About two hours later lightning struck a nearby tree and there was a clap of thunder that sounded like the crack of doom.

My patient woke up very much frightened. So was I. I said, "Looks like we will all go to heaven together now." He raised up on his elbow, looked himself over by the light of the next flash, and said, "I sure would cut a fine figure in heaven with a lady's nightgown on and my throat cut!"

I assured him that St. Peter was accustomed to strange sights at the Golden Gate.

The storm let up after a while. My patient dropped off to sleep. The next morning he showed a considerable will to live, and it looked as if he might. Maybe the lightning scared him out of hankering for eternity.

So I saddled my horse and rode home.

When it wasn't rainy and muddy it was dry and dusty. One summer, the hottest summer I ever witnessed, there was not a speck of rain. The dirt roads (there was no pavement, or even graveled roads) were shoe-mouth deep in dust. This did not keep the community from having its annual picnic. This was a three-day affair. There were watermelons, "ice-cold lemonade made in the shade and stirred with a golden spade," popcorn and peanuts, and barbecue.

There were a few minor fights the first two days of the picnic, nothing that required surgery. Then came Saturday, the closing day, when the picnickers were getting tired and their tempers were getting short. It wound up in a free-for-all.

In the melee, a two hundred-pound blacksmith, young and vigorous, suffered a ten-inch knife wound across the upper part of his abdomen. The cut was something like surgeons would make today in upper abdominal surgery such as gall bladder and stomach surgery. There was a cut across the liver about five inches long. His small bowels came out.

Well, to make a long story short, the picnickers wrapped up the intestines in an old jumper, put the man into a buggy and brought him to my office for me to sew him up. It was a pretty nasty job with dirt, dust, dung and everything else in the wound. I washed off the intestines with a warm saline solution, flushed out the abdomen with the same solution, sewed up the cut in the liver and closed the abdomen. I expected infection.

But do you know, there was not a particle of infection. In ten days the village smithy was back in his shop. He lived to fight another day.

In a killing usually it was a badman who did it. And "badman" is one word, not two, just like "damyankee" is one word. The badman would decide to add another notch to his gun. When a man kills another he becomes a changed man. He becomes a dangerous man. He is a dangerous man to argue with.

Most old-timers came to know that, so that a man who had killed once, whether the fight was fair or foul, was given a wide range. Usually, some stranger to the ways of gunmen was the unfortunate victim. The killer added another notch to his gun with the same inward satisfaction that another man might feel in some act of bravery, sportsmanship or endurance. Texas produced several notorious killers. They were all cowards. They say Texans are braggarts, but we can't brag on our pioneer crop of gunmen, Hollywood to the contrary.

The movies and some writers of the so-called wild West tend to dramatize and glamorize the old-time gun fighters, especially those who ranged in Texas. Most of this stuff is pure-dee bunk. They tell about the split-second draw, the hammer fanners and Deadeye-Dicks who fired two guns from the hips. All of this is greatly exaggerated, if not pure fiction.

When I came to Texas, many men still carried pistols, some concealed and some in holsters out in the open.

Now, there was a difference between a shooting scrape and a killing scrape.

In the shootings, two fellows would meet just anywhere, usually in the street or at a fence row, and begin exchanging shots. I never observed any courtesy shown each other as to the so-called fair or even draw. Each fellow went for his gun and the battle was on. Frequently when their six-shooters were empty and the smoke cleared away, both shooters could be seen walking away from the battleground. Sometimes one of them would be down, wounded, but very rarely dead. The average gun-toter was a very bad shot, especially if he was being shot at himself.

Around Holland there were quite a few gun-toters. Some of these characters would tank up and then decide to settle an old grudge. I believe I heard the noisiest shooting scrape ever pulled off in that part of Texas. There was an old blacksmith shop, its roof and sides of corrugated iron. A couple of fellows who had threatened to shoot each other met in the blacksmith shop. One of them had a six-shooter and the other had two six-shooters. That made eighteen cartridges. When they started blazing away at each other the tin sides and roof of that old shop screeched and screamed and bulged. Smoke rolled out of the door and oozed through the bullet holes. The roar was something that conditioned me for the roar of battle in France years later. Well, sir, you know when it was all over, one of those fellows had a flesh wound, and that was all.

And here's a little triangle. Near town there was a cotton farmer and he had a tenant on his place. The tenant began paying too much attention to a girl who was picking cotton on the place. The landowner did not like that. The tenant had a .45-caliber six-shooter. He already was a good shot, but he went out and practiced shooting, late in the afternoon, two or three times a week. Finally the two of them met, not in the cotton field, but in front of a drugstore in town. The landowner had a .38-caliber pistol. They started shooting, at about twenty feet, all the time dodging behind hitching racks, awnings and other shelters. When the guns were empty, one bullet had nicked the landowner in the heel. I asked why they couldn't do any better than that, and they seemed a little bit ashamed of themselves.

Baseball rhubarbs were a common occurrence. It seemed that every time the home-town team lost a game the visiting team had to beat them again in a free-for-all.

My first case was a twenty-year-old pitcher whose head had been "busted" by a bat in the hands of a batter whom he had fanned for the third time. This fellow had a skull fracture. A piece of bone about one inch long and one inch wide had been knocked into his brain. A hematoma formed. A hematoma is a swelling or tumor filled with blood that has escaped from its proper channel. His injury was on the left side of the head, over a fissure that we call the rolando. He began to have convulsions two or three times a day. In a kitchen-table job I removed the piece of bone that had been driven into his head. His fits stopped. Although he had a residual paralysis in his right leg, it improved steadily.

There were accidents, too.

Two little boys were digging worms for fish bait, one of them doing the digging and the other grabbing the wigglers. The larger of the boys, wielding the grubbing hoe, uncovered a particularly fine specimen. The younger boy, with his mind on what a fine fish the worm would fetch, grabbed for the worm. In that split second the grubbing hoe came down on his head. A piece of bone the size of a silver dollar was driven into the brain. The wound was full of dirt. Ordinarily such a wound could be expected to be fatal. I removed the bone, cleaned out the wound and packed it with antiseptic gauze. The boy got well and grew up to be a preacher—and an unusually good one.

Another boy was kicked by a mule and suffered the same type of fracture. The same procedure brought the same results except that he did not become a preacher.

One bright, moonlight morning about two o'clock I was called to a farmer's house. His wife had been shot in the right frontal portion of her head with a .38-caliber pistol. Her husband stated that it was a mistake. His story was that his wife, clad in a nightgown, had gone outdoors while he was asleep. As she climbed the creaky steps to re-enter the house he was awakened. He thought she was one of those white-robed night riders who were terrorizing the country in connection with stock laws and labor troubles. He pulled his pistol from under his pillow and fired. Since the couple were devoted to each other I had no reason to doubt his account of the incident, and I did not report it to authorities. In a way, the pioneer doctor was a bit of a lawman.

But my business was to do something about the bullet wound, which was just above the hairline a little to the right. There was no exit wound. From the husband's description of the accident, including the fact that he fired while the figure was stooped over, I concluded that the bullet had gone through brain tissue and was lodged somewhere on the inside of the base of the skull. After doing what I could to overcome shock and applying an antiseptic dressing, I went after emergency equipment and asked for help from the nearest surgical center. The X-ray showed the bullet flattened out on the base of the skull. We removed several pieces of bone, one deep in brain tissue. We packed a whole yard of gauze into the cavity, applied bandages and dressing, and left her in the hands of the fates. The bullet never was removed. Believe it or not, she recovered and lived another thirty years.

By virtue of my own varied practice and of observation of others, I felt that I was getting along very well in skull surgery. Also I did quite a few abdominal operations.

But I ran into difficulty. That part of the country was pretty much in the goiter belt. Several cases came to me for attention, and I didn't know what to do about them. One especially bad case was a forty-year-old woman who had choking spells. Her family would get alarmed, thinking she was about to strangle, and they would send for me. But after I got out there I didn't know what to do for her. I knew of no effective goiter remedy.

I read in a magazine that there was a Northern doctor who was operating for goiter, and, according to the magazine writer, he was very successful. His name was Charles H. Mayo, who was associated with his brother, Dr. William J. Mayo, and their father, Dr. William W. Mayo. I told my partner, Dr. Goddard, I would have to go up to Rochester to see what the Mayos were doing.

All of them were very kind to me, and Dr. Charles let me mask and gown up every morning and stand by in the operating room while he did several goiter operations.

Then he told me to go to the University of Chicago Medical School, procure a cadaver with a goiter and practice on it. He suggested that I take out the goiter just as I had observed the procedure in the operating room. I did so, and then returned to Texas, feeling that I had a working knowledge of the subject. I was broke again, but I knew I had made some progress.

That must have been about 1904 or 1905. The first

patient was the woman who had had choking spells. The operation was a complete removal of the thyroid gland; bilateral thyroidectomy, surgeons call it. I believe that was the first goiter operation in Texas, and I am sure it was the first complete thyroidectomy done in the Southwest.

Word had got around that I was going to butcher a woman from ear to ear, and I had quite an audience. It reminded me of the occasion, several years previously, when I took that tumor out of Aunt Bess. My partner assisted me, and the neighbors formed a fly-swatting brigade. The operation was a success.

Today I believe there is a definite trend toward the limitation or abandonment of surgery for goiter. But the idea of operating certainly was in vogue in the mid-1900s.

Consequently my practice flourished, and my reputation spread. Frank Harrison McGregor, son of a local dentist, became a protégé of mine and I employed him as a bookkeeper. Later he graduated in medicine and went on up to Mangum, Oklahoma, where he formed a partnership with Dr. George Fowler Border, the same man who had been largely responsible for my start in medical practice at Holland.

During one summer there seemed to be an unusually large number of goiter cases in the Mangum area. Dr. McGregor told Dr. Border about the success I had been having in Texas with goiter operations.

So they invited me up there to read a paper and put on a clinic before the Western Oklahoma District Medical Society. They had six cases worked up, the proper tests made, and ready for surgery. I did the operations in the forenoon, ate a big chicken dinner, read my paper, and went back home that night. There was no charge for my services.

However, the six patients sent me a fine watch with their names engraved on the inside of the lid.

Dr. Border telephoned me one day that there was a woman there who would not let him operate, but that she would consent to let "that big doctor from Texas" do the job.

"They've got plenty of money, too," Border added.

It was four hundred miles up there, but I undertook the trip.

The patient was the old-maid daughter of a man, who, it seemed to me, owned most of the county. He was county sheriff, too; wore a big badge and carried a .30-caliber automatic Winchester.

We operated the morning after my arrival.

After the job was done, the sheriff said, "What am I going to owe you?"

I answered, "You mean, 'What do you owe me?' not what are you 'going to owe me?' "

He laughed, and guessed that was right.

I told him that big shots would have charged him $2,000, and I thought I ought to have half that much.

I didn't think I was overcharging him, according to his means. For poorer folks I did the same operation for $100 or less, and in some cases I got nothing. If I had done the same for the wealthy sheriff he would have been insulted; he would not have appreciated my services, and he would not have been able to understand why I could afford to leave my own patients and journey up to Oklahoma to operate on his daughter. So when I said, "half of $2,000," I was helping maintain his ego as well as my prestige and solvency. One way to look at it was that I was treating the sheriff as well as his daughter.

The sheriff reached into his pocket and brought out a greasy looking checkbook and the stump of a pencil. There was a flunky hanging around there by the name of Jeff.

The sheriff said, "Get down, Jeff." Jeff got down on his all-fours. The sheriff squatted down beside Jeff, placed the checkbook on Jeff's back, and wrote me a check for $1,000.

"Well, here ye air," he said. "If ye don't get yer money the fust time run 'er through the bank again."

The check was good the first time I put it in the bank.

I didn't always fare so well from the standpoint of prestige and pay. You may have to hold your nose for this one.

One of my early surgical operations was for drainage of an abscess caused by a ruptured, gangrenous appendix. The patient had survived his acute peritonitis, but the entire lower abdomen was filled, more or less, with a wall of abscess.

The family doctor had diagnosed the case as abdominal tumor. I was called to the small village, about twenty-five miles from my office, to operate. By cautious questioning of one of the cowboys, who was an older brother of the patient, I learned that the fourteen-year-old boy had been seized with a severe, cramping pain in the pit of his stomach, followed by vomiting and fever.

I also ascertained from the brother that the doctor had given the patient a big dose of castor oil and followed through with two big blue mass pills (purgative). I found the patient quite ill. He had been stricken twelve days previously.

In spite of all the symptoms, the doctor still contended it was a belly tumor. I tried to convince him that the large mass was an abscess, due to a ruptured, gangrenous appendix and localized peritonitis. But no, it had to be a tumor.

My first impulse was to go home.

However, the boy's life was at stake. The only thing doctors knew to do at that time was to drain, to get in and out as quickly as possible.

The family doctor agreed to drop the chloroform. A practical nurse from the neighborhood was engaged to fan off the flies. I made a quick short incision. The foulest pus I had ever encountered spouted up. Colon bacilli and feces poured out, adding to the sickening odor. The nurse fainted. The old doctor, who was dozing with his head down in the chloroform fumes, roused up and got a whiff of the pus and, in a loud voice exclaimed, "Cut a gut, by golly." I tried to explain, but the doctor kept mumbling, "He cut a gut, by golly."

I finished the operation, but left in bad repute so far as that family and the neighborhood were concerned. They did not offer to pay me.

The boy got well. A few months later he and his cowboy brother rode in to see me. They paid me a modest fee for the operation and said their doctor admitted he had been wrong.

There were times, too, when it seemed to me that the country doctor was taken too much for granted.

Oftentimes we were awakened in the middle of the night by someone shouting, "Hello!" at the front gate. Usually it was the biggest boy or the hired hand who had hurried off to town after the doctor.

"Hello, Doc!" came the voice from the darkness. "You are wanted at So-and-So's house."

"What's the trouble?"

"I don't know."

"How bad off are they?"

"I don't know."

So there was nothing to do but saddle up old Buck and go out.

I remember one dark rainy night I answered such a call about ten miles from town. When I got there I found the old man sawing away at his fiddle. He spat a squirt of tobacco juice into the fireplace and said, "Come in, Doc, make yourself at home."

He started into "Durango's March." I broke in with, "Who is sick?"

The old man halted his fiddlin' just long enough to explain. "Well, last night the baby had the croup and we just didn't want to take chances of him having it again tonight without a doctor around, so we sent after you. You know, Doc, a pint o' prevention is worth a peck o' cure."

I rode off, wondering why I ever wanted to be a doctor anyway.

THOSE DEVIL WAGONS

I AM going to take you from the horse-drawn economy into the age of the motor vehicle. Those whose memories don't go back that far missed something. But, like a motion picture, the whole works is being repeated in this nuclear age, except on a grander scale.

Younger generations are likely to assume that nuclear energy represents the millennium, that man has achieved the ultimate in creation and destruction. We forget that other discoveries and inventions, in their early days, were quite as impressive and awesome to people of those days as atomic developments are to us today.

Steam and gasoline were worthy forerunners of atomic power. In our part of the country, steam gave us the powered cotton gin and the railroad locomotive, and gasoline gave us the automobile. Steam boilers ran gins which had been powered by treadmill-like arrangements, using oxen, or, in still earlier days, manpower. Powered cotton gins, in turn, made possible an extensive textile industry, which put shirts on the backs of the heathen. The railroad locomotive, along with the steamboat, fitted into this system of making and moving goods.

There was some opposition. More than one Southern

town was bypassed by the railroads because the residents did not take kindly to the iron horse. The soot, they complained, would soil the crinoline of the plantation belles. There were those who said the smoke from locomotives would leave a trail of tuberculosis along the railroad right-of-way. Die-hard trail drivers claimed cattle would lose weight in the cars whereas they gained weight by grazing along the trail to market.

Many farmers, too, thought the railroads were the devil's handiwork. I don't know whether it was true or not, but railroads were blamed for bringing Johnson grass to Texas. The theory was that in hauling grain from the Johnson-grass-ridden Middle West, some of the grain—and grass seed—spilled along the railroad right-of-way. There the Johnson grass took root and gradually spread to nearby fields, and once it got a foothold in a community, farm animals and birds and the wind would distribute the seed over a wide area. If you know Johnson grass you know it is the bane of Southern fields today—a cancerous growth in fertile soil. Whether the railroads were responsible or not, they got the blame.

Some lawyers made a lucrative practice out of lawsuits against railway companies. Let a scrub cow get killed by a train and she immediately became a fine-blooded animal at the courthouse. It was easy to collect damages from the big corporations, especially if you had a jury of farmers who had been fighting Johnson grass.

It was in this atmosphere that the auto made its advent in Texas. Manufacturers advertised their products as "horseless carriages," but many others termed them "devil wagons." A more elegant name for a car was "the thing."

The coming of the automobile gave impetus to oil production and refining. There were those who said that drilling holes in the earth and letting the planet's natural lubricant gush forth might have serious consequences on the earth's movements. Others prophesied that the withdrawal of the oil would cause the upper crust of the earth to collapse and that the seas would rush in. Still others warned that if man did not quit probing the earth a spark would ignite the subterranean deposits of oil and blow us all to kingdom come.

I guess I contributed my share to impending doom. I bought an automobile. I figured that if we were going to be blown up anyway, I might as well travel in style. I bought the first automobile in Holland, and the local ginner bought the second. Mine was a model F Buick. It had two cylinders; I remember that feature because Buick was advertising, "We do with two cylinders what others try with four." It was cranked on the side. It had carbide-gas lights. It had a chain drive, and it could easily make forty miles an hour on good, level, dry roads provided it did not flip the chain or run over a stump and have a blowout.

The farmers complained that the newfangled horseless carriages frightened their livestock. However, I found that it was the natives themselves, rather than their animals, who were afraid of the things.

On one occasion I had to make a medical call about forty miles from town. The roads were winding and narrow. I ran over a stump and tore off the muffler. That engine made a racket like a threshing machine. My brakes were bad, too. I started down a long hill lined with Johnson grass higher than the car. As I gained momentum I heard someone yelling near the foot of the hill. I could not stop, or even slow up.

When I got near the bottom of the hill I saw a farmer with two scrub ponies hitched to a wagonload of women and children. He had pulled the wagon off to the side of the road. He was busy pitching children over the fence as if they were cordwood. He figured the team was going to run away and scatter women and children in the path of the on-coming monster. Instead, when I got alongside him, the team, unperturbed, was eating ravenously of the Johnson grass. The farmer was the one who was frightened.

As I shot by, the old man jumped aside and yelled, "Go it, you rich devil!"

I was conscious of the class distinction he had made.

Maybe I lost some business by promoting myself from a horse-and-buggy doctor to a devil-wagon doctor. But I could cover a larger territory and attend to emergencies much faster.

I remember one call from a farmer's home about two miles from town. There was some kind of surgical emergency, I was told. On this occasion all went well with my devil wagon and within ten minutes I was at the farm.

And such a mess I had never seen. There was a dead bulldog on the floor. The kids were crying, apparently over the dead dog rather than over their daddy, who was on the bed with his clothes partially off and bleeding like the proverbial stuck pig.

The furniture was disarranged. There were sticks of firewood scattered about. The housewife, face and hands scratched, was flustered and angry. She was trying to pry open the set jaws of the bulldog.

As near as the incident could be reconstructed, this was what had happened:

The head of the household had been in town. He came

home feeling frolicsome after having a few beers with his friends. His pockets were stuffed with candy, chewing gum, nuts and apples for the children. As soon as he entered the house the kids ganged him and began to rob his pockets. He entered into the spirit of the thing and began grabbing the children as they came near him and piling them up in a heap.

He was stooping down and holding his struggling brood on the floor when the bulldog, the children's guardian, decided it was time to take a hand in the rough-and-tumble. So he made a lunge and grabbed the old man in the seat of the pants.

The dog held on and that was when the real ruckus started. The wife began beating the dog with sticks of wood while the man was swinging him around the room, upsetting the furniture. The children pitched in and tried to pull the dog off. The man finally managed to tear himself free, but the dog was dead. The woman had bashed in his head with a piece of firewood. But, even in death, the dog held tenaciously onto his bite—and that was where I came in.

The man was badly lacerated and torn in a rather vital spot. I patched him up as well as I could, but I never made another obstetrical call to that home.

The point is, though, if it had not been for my Buick that man might have bled to death.

Steam, as I have said, was pictured as another herald of doomsday. Every once in a while a boiler in a railroad locomotive or on a steamboat would explode, and there would be maimed and dead. In most cases these things happened out on the prairie or on a river. They were just something we read about in the newspapers and didn't mean much to us until we had the big boiler explosion at the gin in Holland.

Along about the middle of September, the gin was running full blast, night and day. A boiler blew up—biggest noise I had ever heard. The concussion shook windows in homes all over town. I was eating lunch at home when it happened. I ran outside. Pieces of brick and iron and wood were falling in the yard. Teams were running wild; everyone was running and yelling. That is, those who were able to run and yell. There were two dead and ten seriously injured. Mrs. Doctor and I turned our little home into an emergency hospital.

One of the victims was the ginner himself. He had multiple skull fractures and deep face burns. His was a long and precarious recovery.

A few years later, when he was well recovered, he purchased an automobile. Maybe he thought gasoline was safer than steam. He delighted in taking the ladies riding in the thing, especially for their first ride.

Now there was my Aunt Susie. She would never ride with me; her daily prediction was that I would get killed driving that thing. But she consented to ride with the ginner, provided I would go along just in case of accident. She wanted a doctor handy. We drove out in the country a couple of miles and then she decided that was enough. The driver undertook to turn around in the road, which was bordered by tall Johnson grass and a three-strand barbed-wire fence.

Something happened to the mechanism, and the car shot through the high weeds, knocked down a fencepost and wound up in a wheat field. Aunt Susie was the calmest one in the car. She casually asked the driver why he had driven out into the wheat field. By that time the ginner had recovered his wits. He replied, "Oh, just to turn around." He headed back to the road and toward town.

There is nothing like nonchalance in a tense situation. Sometimes we ought to stay put instead of running after trouble. I can tell you a story about that, too.

Diagonally across the street from our house there was a greasy-spoon chili joint, run by a tall, skinny fellow, six feet four, weight about 130 pounds, and his 230-pound wife. One July evening Mrs. Crosthwait and I were seated on our front lawn, trying to catch a breath of fresh air. We heard a terrible racket across the street in the chili parlor. Pans were rattling. Bang, bong, bang! A woman was yelling at the top of her voice, "You're killin' me, you're killin' me!"

My wife said, "Doctor, that man is beating that woman to death."

I said, "She can take care of herself."

"Are you going to let him kill her?"

My wife urged me. "Hurry, get over there. You are afraid, are you? If so, I'll go."

That was a challenge to the chivalry and gallantry of a Southern gentleman. I could not ignore it.

I rushed over. The skinny husband had his buxom wife down on the floor and was pounding her with his fists. She was clawing like a tomcat entangled in a fish net.

I was skinny, too, but rather active, and I grabbed him by the seat of his overalls. I pulled him off the woman and shoved him out the back door.

Now, according to all the storybooks about when knighthood was in flower, the damsel saved in distress always had some reward for her rescuer. I should have got a bucket of chili out of it anyway.

But not from the princess of the chili castle. She jumped

up and quick as a flash grabbed a tin washpan, slammed me across the shoulders with it and shouted, "Get out of here, you two-story son of a gun."

Well, that wasn't exactly what she said—"son of a gun" —but let's let it go at that; it looks better in print.

About the same time that mechanical progress was bringing us the automobile, medical advancement was proving some vaccines.

This period—the last years of the first decade of the twentieth century—meant a great deal in my career. For the first time I began to feel confident that the inadequacy of my medical education had been overcome and this I attributed to the postgraduate courses I had taken in leading clinics and hospitals.

Medical knowledge was being disseminated more widely. Take the case of typhoid, which had killed my elder brother years previously. When I first went to Texas the diagnosis of typhoid fever was by smell. Preventative and curative agents were nonexistent or inadequate.

I recall the case of a sixteen-year-old girl. A young general practitioner, not long out of college, was called. He was unable to make a diagnosis. He called in a resident doctor from a hospital and they were unable to arrive at a conclusion. Finally there were four of us in consultation.

An old doctor walked up to the bed, greeted the patient, felt her hair, got one whiff of the odor and said to us, "How long has she had this typhoid fever?" We looked blank. We retired to the parlor for another consultation. The old doctor explained that he had detected the smell of typhoid the second he stepped into the room. Confirming his first impression were the dry hair and skin, the foul matter on the teeth, the patient's position in bed and her listlessness.

The girl survived due more to her own powers of resistance than to anything we could do for her.

In the late summer and autumn of 1908, I think it was, a rather widespread epidemic of typhoid fever occurred in the Holland territory. It had been a long, dry, hot summer. Water was scarce, wells were dry, and water holes were very low and probably polluted. It seemed to me that there was a case of typhoid in almost every home, and in some families there were several cases.

I learned that the United States Public Health Service was about to release a vaccine for prevention and possible cure of typhoid. I requested a supply to vaccinate persons who had been exposed to the disease, and all others who volunteered. The serum was supplied promptly, at government expense, and my associate and I proceeded to vaccinate a thousand persons. We kept a list of those vaccinated, and the dates of their vaccinations. At the same time we kept a list of persons who had been exposed similarly, or were living in proximity to cases, who for reasons of their own refused to be inoculated. Two years later we were able to report that among the thousand persons vaccinated only two cases of typhoid fever had occurred. Among an equal number who refused to be vaccinated there were thirty cases of the disease within the two-year period. The epidemic gradually faded away.

So far as I know that was the first typhoid prophylaxis practiced in Texas.

It was obvious that the answer to the typhoid problem was not cure, but prevention through use of vaccine. Today vaccination is routine, and there are many young doctors who have never seen a case of typhoid fever.

There were other health problems crying for attention,

and it looked to me as if it was going to take some political activity to help solve them.

It was about that time, 1908, that I got into politics in a modest sort of way. For governor I supported Thomas M. Campbell and when he was elected he appointed me a delegate to the International Congress on Tuberculosis, which met in Washington, D.C. The congress, the first of several, was called after tests had shown that almost every adult in densely populated countries had the bacilli of tuberculosis, a disease of both man and beast.

There were twenty-six nations represented at the congress, including Russia and Japan. The sessions were not restricted to tuberculosis, but dealt with various ailments.

Among those present was Dr. Edward Trudeau, who had suffered from TB himself and had become an advocate of open-air treatment. He was credited with changing "sanitarium" to "sanatorium." The latter term came to be applied to a hospital especially designed and equipped to take care of tubercular patients.

I was sold on the idea of institutional treatment for such patients. I wrote a paper on the advantages of that treatment in Texas and suggested the establishment of an institution in our state. The idea was destined to take me into politics.

There were four candidates for governor in 1908, including Oscar B. Colquitt of Kaufman, Texas.

I decided it was a good time to do something about a sanatorium for Texas.

The precinct convention of the Democratic party was held in the street in front of my office. I introduced a resolution urging party support for the establishment of a sanatorium. It passed. I was named a delegate to the county convention. I maneuvered to get myself appointed to the platform committee, and got my resolution adopted. It was worded to recommend a state appropriation of $200,000 to build a sanatorium near San Angelo, Texas, and also to recommend the establishment of a state board of health. Some colleagues in the medical profession lined up with me. Opponents included Jim Ferguson, who was destined to become a stormy petrel in Texas politics.

Jim told the convention, "Dr. Crosthwait! Why, that country doctor don't know nothing about legislation!"

What some of those fellows wanted was to spend the money their own way.

At the state convention the members of the platform committee retired to a little room in one of the big hotels in San Antonio and I offered my resolution. A doctor from East Texas seconded it. But it was voted down in the final report of the committee. However, we managed to get the resolution into the minority report.

When the committee reported to the convention, Morris Sheppard, then in Congress, bobbed up in favor of the resolution to establish a sanatorium and a state board of health. I made the only political speech of my life. It may have been Senator Sheppard's moving speech that did it. At any rate, the will of the convention appeared to be favorable.

However, when the platform came out finally, it made no mention of the sanatorium or of the state board of health.

But both these demands became law under the administration of Governor Colquitt.

You see, we had not put all our eggs into the convention basket. I had written a questionnaire to all four candidates for the Democratic nomination for governor. I wrote to every doctor in Texas, and the story of the movement was printed in the state medical journal.

Colquitt was the only candidate who answered the questionnaire, and he pledged his support to both projects. He became the Democratic nominee and his pledges, although not in the platform, were made good in the form of legislation. The State Board of Health was organized and the Carlsbad tubercular institution, now called the McKnight Sanatorium, was established at Sanatorium, Texas, near San Angelo.

I attribute this result not to my own efforts, but more to a little political activity and the seemingly inconsequential fact that the governor had named me a delegate to the international meeting of great doctors.

Before I leave this topic I want to mention another indirect result of that conference within my own experience.

A doctor from the Carolinas, who also was a delegate, brought a patient to the conference. He was a white tenant farmer, about thirty. He had eruptions on his hands, face and chest. His tongue was red and his mouth inflamed. He was extremely nervous. He had nausea and diarrhea, and, during the first few days of his illness, he had fever. He had been ailing ten days when he was brought to Washington to be viewed by that distinguished company. It was concluded that the Carolina farmer had acute pellagra. The disease was prevalent in the Southern states, but diagnosis usually was erroneous.

Shortly after I returned home from the Washington conference I was called to Pine Bluff, Arkansas, to see a patient, the son of a ranchman. The town was in an uproar. There had not been so much excitement since a federal judge sentenced six outlaws to be hanged in the courtyard.

The patient, a short time previously, had embarked on a

small furniture-manufacturing enterprise. He was a single man and was living in a hotel on the main street of the town. When he was stricken the hotel was quarantined. The quarantine sign said, "Smallpox." At the drugstore there was gossip that it was not smallpox at all; that some terrible new disease had come in. They said the fellow was all broken out and as wild as a drunken Indian.

I looked for the doctor in charge of the case and was advised that he was quarantined inside the hotel with his patient. I was told that I could go in to see the patient, but that I could not come back out of the hotel until the quarantine was lifted. I went in, saw the patient, got a brief history of the case from the doctor, and told him I thought it was acute pellagra.

"Well, I'll be damned!" he said. "Why didn't I think of that? I just read about that pellagra in a medical journal last week."

We got the patient quieted down and placed a male nurse in charge.

Then we called the mayor and the city physician and convinced them that there was no need for quarantine. The hotel opened for business that afternoon. The newspaper came out with a front-page announcement that a famous specialist from Texas had diagnosed the case as pellagra, and that there was no cause for alarm.

Several persons who thought they had been exposed and feared they might be getting pellagra tried to make appointments to see me. I slipped quietly out of town. The man got well under the care of his local doctor.

Now I want to take you, for the time being, from individual ills to an instance of mass hysteria.

In 1910 a natural phenomenon gripped our community

and the world at large. Probably nothing comparable to it occurred for another forty years when we had the Martian invasions and flying saucers.

Our excitement was due to Halley's comet. Years previously an English astronomer, Edmund Halley (1656–1742) predicted that a comet which had been reappearing for centuries would show up again in 1835, in 1910 and in 1985, at intervals of 75 years.

I am told Halley's comet made its appearance in 1835. I know it came in 1910 because I, and millions of others now living, saw it.

For centuries the appearance of comets had been associated, in the human mind, with plagues, famines and wars. The reappearance of Halley's comet in 1910 was no exception. Some experts told us that if the comet slipped a cog and struck the earth it would wipe us out. It wasn't a very pleasant prospect just at the time when we were enjoying such fruits of civilization as the automobile.

In our part of the country earthly thinking came to a jolting halt, all on account of an egg.

About eight miles southeast of Holland there was a little settlement called Science Hill. It consisted of a school, a church, a brush-arbor tabernacle, a store and a blacksmith shop. There were a half dozen residences scattered about within a radius of a half mile of the hamlet.

A week or so before Halley's comet was due one of the housewives found a strange egg in a hen nest. Inscribed on that egg, in fine Spencerian hand, was the message: "Prepare for the comet."

In the state of mind that most of the residents were in, that could be only a message from On High. The Science Hill school dismissed immediately, and pupils went to see the egg with the doomsday message. Parents came, too, and then kept their children at home so the families could be together when the end came.

There was a lot of praying because there had been a lot of backsliding. That must have been along about the first part of April and it had been a long time since the last revival, the preceding July. An itinerant preacher had come in there during the winter, but he ran away with a farmer's wife, who was the church organist.

All in all, when the egg with the ominous message was found that community was pretty well steeped in sin.

People from all around Science Hill—from Holland, Bartlett, Austin, Temple and Waco—came to see that egg, and many went away converted. The miracle egg put Science Hill on the map.

There was a suicide or two, and maybe a mental case or so, but I feel safe in saying that the egg made more Christians than it killed. At least, for the time being there was a great fear of the wrath of the Lord.

Well, Halley's comet came, and for several weeks it shone down on us, without incident. It looked like a glowing ball with a sparkling tail.

And Halley's comet went away.

Long afterwards the village smithy admitted he had perpetrated the hoax with the message on the egg.

I saw another omen, this one on the horizon. It was a come-hither beacon.

Fifty miles to the north of Holland was Waco. I had about made up my mind that my boyhood dream of landing in Chicago, Philadelphia or New York was not likely to materialize soon. But Waco had something to offer. Only recently completed was the Amicable Building, a twenty-two-story skyscraper advertised as "The tallest building in the Southwest." This edifice stuck out high above the surrounding cotton fields, and on very clear nights you could see the lights from afar. Besides that, Waco, with a population of thirty or forty thousand, I guess, had some fine schools, churches and hospitals. It was something that a country doctor would aspire to.

I had my mind's eye on that fine city and that tall building when I had a stroke of misfortune.

I had an attack of acute mastoiditis which required radical surgery and months of convalescence. After the surgery I lapsed into unconsciousness. I had developed a bloodstream infection.

It was during this time that I had a dream, or rather a nightmare, which has always fascinated me. I had read of the Pyramids in Egypt, but had never seen them. In my feverish brain, though, I took a trip to the great Pyramid of Cheops. There I was stripped of all my clothing, robed in colorful regalia, and was required to undergo a long period of ritualistic routine.

Then I was led down a long corridor, down and down, until we came to a large room, dimly lit. Here I was required to take an oath not to reveal any secrets of the place. There were many dignitaries wearing glittering robes set with what looked like millions of diamonds. Each of these patriarchs carried a gleaming sword or dagger.

After they looked me over I had to pass through a long line of guards almost as lavishly garbed and armed. Then I was detained. For days, it seemed to me, the elders debated the question of what they should do with me. At least that was what I gathered from their talk, which was a strange tongue to me. Finally, in English the head man asked me where I came from and what was I doing there. I explained that I was from the U.S.A. and all I wanted was the secret of making concrete such as they had used in the construction of the Pyramids. Just why I wanted that information was not clear to me, either, unless it was to build a bigger skyscraper in the Southwest.

Again I was escorted down and down into an inner chamber far more brilliant than the other. There were more richly clothed and heavily armed guards and dignitaries.

I was seated in the center of the group. I was approached by a very large man with a long white beard and a solemn expression. He told me that I was about to be given the pyramid builders' secret recipe for concrete, but that I was never to divulge it to anyone.

He handed me a sealed envelope and at the same time struck me on the top of my head with a mallet. I saw stars and flashes of light, and when I came to, my wife was sitting by my bedside.

The nurse said, "Doctor, you have been asleep for fifteen days." That was her way of breaking it gently to me that I had been unconscious that long.

The time was wasted, too, because I didn't learn a thing about building pyramids.

I was disabled for three months after the operation.

And I was on the rocks, financially. We experienced a short-lived panic and bank moratorium. Equities which I had built up in various properties disappeared. It became difficult for me to meet my financial obligations.

We had two children, Robert Wilson, born in 1904, and Marylu Border, 1905, and their future, as well as my surgical ambitions, were at stake.

Taking stock of the situation I had to admit that my practice in Holland had been good. The books showed a thousand obstetrical cases and several hundred operations during the period 1898–1910. Considering that in many cases I had to travel long distances to reach my patients, the figures were impressive. At the same time there were poor-paying patients and there was some loss of practice due to my own illness. Also, I must admit, my repeated trips to clinical centers in Chicago, Cleveland, Rochester, Boston, New York and Baltimore had taken some of our savings. We considered these trips a necessary investment, though, to make up for my inadequate medical education.

By and by, my health improved somewhat, my practice picked up again and we began recovering financially. The bright lights of the city beckoned again.

I thought I had reached that stage in my profession that patients ought to begin coming to me instead of my riding out after them horseback, or with horse and buggy or even with the Buick. Highway improvements were coming right along, and there was no reason why they should not come to see me once the prejudice against those devil wagons was broken down.

UP TO THE CITY

So in 1911 we traded our Holland house for a farm and then turned around and traded the farm for a house in Waco. We packed up everything and moved in a boxcar. That included our milk cow and horse and buggy. The Buick had gone by the board in our financial reverses. I had thirty-five dollars in cash and two letters of credit from my banker in Holland. I knew one family in Waco and had a slight acquaintanceship with a couple of doctors whom I had met at medical conventions.

But I put up a bold front. I leased an office in the twenty-two-story building, about midway up, as high as I could get. That halfway-up location was sort of symbolic to me; I had come a long way, but I had a long way to go yet.

A few days after I opened my office I got a bit of a letdown. One of the old-timers there whom I had met at a medical meeting accosted me as I came out of an elevator. He greeted me:

"Well, I see another country doctor has come to town to do surgery. You can always tell a country doctor. He has manure on his shoes, amber (tobacco juice) on his shirt front and an important case to talk about. Ha, ha, ha!"

I had heard that old jibe before. It was not the kind of

welcome I expected from a colleague in the medical fraternity.

By way of encouragement he added, "Well, son, if you can finance yourself that long, I'll give you a year to stay here. I've seen them come and go for the past forty years."

I was a bit shocked, but thanked him and said, "Doctor, I came here to stay."

At this point in my narrative I come to a little sentimental journey. You may skip the next three or four paragraphs without losing the thread of my story, but I am going to tell this anyway, and I intend to document it. A few months after we left Holland more than four hundred citizens of that village and vicinity signed a petition that, "Having known you in your practice in our homes and county, realizing your most excellent ability as a physician and surgeon and also your good citizenship, we desire you to return to our town for permanent location."

The petition and the signatures covered an entire page of the *Holland Progress,* issue of February 2, 1912. And the editor, J. S. Hair, added, "It is as the *Progress* stated last fall when the doctor left—'no one ever lived or died in Holland who will be missed by the entire citizenship as will Dr. Crosthwait.' "

I quote these opinions with the greatest humility. I refer to them merely to indicate that any country doctor can enshrine himself in the hearts of his people. I mention it to show it was not easy for me to face hostility in the city when I could have gone back to Holland. Holland was home to us, where I had taught school, where I had married one of my pupils, where I got my start in practice, where Mrs. Doctor became a part of the community, and where our children were born.

As of today, some forty-four years after we left Holland, we are still in Waco. During these years there has been hardly a week that some of my old patients or their descendants or friends have not consulted me. I have operated on hundreds of them.

In the city I realized an ambition I had had for years: Generally speaking, patients came to see me instead of my having to go out to see them. Also I was a few blocks from the hospital instead of many miles. There were interns available as assistants. And there were nurses. It was very seldom now that I had to use my wife as a nurse; it gave her time to attend to our children.

However, the change from kitchen-table surgery to hospital practice was not as abrupt as it might seem. At that time hospitals had not been standardized. Infection had not been brought under control, surgical antiseptic technique was inadequate. So it was difficult to persuade some of our surgical cases to go to the hospitals except in extreme emergencies. With them it was sort of a "last chance" deal. Therefore I had to continue to do home surgery not only in the city but also in homes over the surrounding country for a radius of fifty to one hundred miles. Gradually, the deficiencies in facilities were overcome, people got educated to the advantages of hospital care, and surgical practice settled down to hospitals.

But I have always retained a very wholesome respect for the country doctor. When we speak of country doctors, of course, we mean small-town doctors as well. I have found fewer errors in diagnosis and evaluation of surgical risks by country doctors than by their city counterparts. Many of the city fellows are too prone to depend wholly on the laboratories, the X-rays and the interns to make their diagnosis.

One busy day a country doctor telephoned me from a neighboring town and said, "I am sending in a boy with acute appendicitis. It is a bad case, probably gangrenous, and he should be operated on immediately."

I knew the doctor well. His diagnosis and surgical judgment always had been good. Without further preliminaries, I ordered the boy to surgery as soon as he reached the hospital. I went in, checked his abdomen. There was marked rigidity, pain and tenderness in the right quadrant and a history of nausea and fever.

We had an intern from Puerto Rico who had a poor command of the English language. When we had scrubbed up and gone in to operate he said, "Doctor, what the matter with that boy?"

I said, "Acute appendicitis."

The Puerto Rican said, "Doctor, how you know? No blood count, no examination of urine, no X-ray, no take temperature. How you know he got appendicitis?"

Those were all good questions that called for answers. But I was in a hurry and, for the time being, closed the matter by saying, "A country doctor sent in the boy and he said he had acute appendicitis," and I added an old colloquial expression, "You know you cannot fool a horsefly or a country doctor."

The intern repeated the remark, but appeared somewhat puzzled by the colloquialism.

A few days later the same country doctor telephoned that he was sending in a lady with an acute gall bladder condition and that she required immediate surgery.

Previously I had made a brief examination of the patient in my office and found gallstones which called for an operation, so when she came to the hospital there was not much more for me to do but proceed with the operation.

The same Puerto Rican intern came in to help me. He did not know what had gone on before and he raised the same question as he had in the case of the boy and I said, "Gall bladder disease, gallstones, impending rupture or gangrene."

He said, "Doctor, how can you tell she's got all that?"

I said, "Well, a country doctor sent her in and . . ."

The intern brightened up and said, "Oh, yes, you can't fool a country fly or a horse doctor."

But one of the cases that came from the country turned out to be a rather embarrassing one. It seems that I operated on the "wrong" patient.

A local doctor called me to operate on a patient whose baby he was unable to deliver by the usual methods, all of which had been tried. Such cases are always bad risks. Usually they are beyond the realm of carefully calculated surgical risks; they fall into the class of unpredictable emergencies. However, like any other surgeon, I was ready to pit my reputation against the possibility of saving even one life, and in this instance, two lives were at stake.

So I operated. The patient was a young woman, rather stout, very narrow pelvis. Normal delivery was impossible. The family doctor requested me to resect or tie off the tubes so as to prevent another pregnancy. Such a procedure was legal if, in the judgment of the surgeon, it was indicated. However, I did not agree that it was advisable or quite ethical as I had not consulted with either the patient or her husband. So I delivered the baby, but did nothing to prevent future pregnancies. Mother and baby both did well.

But, believe it or not, the husband was peeved. It developed that he wanted his wife fixed so she would not become pregnant again. His family doctor advised him that he could have a vasectomy done on himself. That is the removal of the vas deferens, which sterilizes the male. He agreed, and I operated on him in my office. I heard no word from him for several months.

Then, one day he showed up, mad as the proverbial wet hen.

He said, "Doc, you done me wrong!"

I was shocked and offended.

"What is your complaint?"

"Well, Doc, my wife is pregnant, and you said it would not happen again."

I said, "My friend, we will make some laboratory tests."

I tested his sterility and it was negative. Then another test with the same result. He was sterile; there was no doubt about it.

I said, "Now, you remember I told you that you would be sterile. I did not tell you that your wife would not become pregnant again."

He looked as if I had hit him with a brick, and he bolted out of the office. I wondered whether his mind was working about like my own.

He worked on a night shift. He went to work at seven p. m. and was off at seven a. m. One night, not long after he had undergone tests at my office, something happened at the plant and he was excused to go home about two a. m. He knocked at the front door and called his wife to let him in. There was a racket in the bedroom and he went around to the back door just in time to see a man, dressed in a long white nightshirt, jump over the back fence. It was his next-door neighbor.

The husband came by to see me the next day and said, "Doc, you operated on the wrong man!"

On another occasion, it looked, for a spell, as if I had

done the wrong operation on the right man. That is, from his standpoint. One of my patrons, a fine old German farmer, came to see me about operating on his son-in-law. He had heard of the sterilization of males in cases of insanity. His son-in-law, the father of three children, had been adjudged insane and sent to a state institution.

Now, the family had been alerted that the patient would be discharged and sent home. It was natural and reasonable that the old gentleman should not want any more grandchildren from what he called "a crazy daddy." So he wanted him sterilized. The same day the young man arrived home from the institution, the father-in-law brought him in to me.

We found what doctors call bilateral varicoceles or varicose veins. That is a varicose enlargement of the veins of the spermatic cord, on both sides. I stressed the desirability of an operation for the correction of this condition. The patient reluctantly consented to the surgery, but he wanted to wait a while. That was exactly what his father-in-law did not want. We finally talked the young man into the operation immediately.

But he still was very uncooperative, so we gave him ether and did a vasectomy along with the varicocele operation.

Things went along very well for a few months. Then some of the young fellows in the neighborhood found out my patient had been sterilized and they began kidding him about it. Apparently he was just about ready to have another blowup anyway.

One dreary, misty afternoon I was alone in our office, sitting at the business desk in the reception room, with my back to the door. I felt the presence of someone. When I looked around I found the crazy would-be daddy standing over me with a six-shooter in his hand.

I have seen a lot of weapons in my time, but never one that looked bigger, uglier and meaner than that pistol did at that time.

My visitor's eyes were flashing fire and his body was trembling like a trapped rabbit. So was mine.

Then he let loose a torrent of profanity and abuse such as I had never heard before. And I've heard some pretty good cussing in my time, too. There was that time when Uncle Slug fell in the slush pit at the molasses mill. And another time, when Uncle Handy got stalled with three yokes of oxen and ten bales of cotton, on the hill near our home. I thought Uncle Handy knew all the bad words, but my patient pulled some new ones on me.

And the patient was so preoccupied in his profanity that he did not pull the trigger. I figured he was saving his bullets until he ran out of cuss words. But before he was through talking, a brother-in-law, who had followed him to town, came in and took him away. The patient went out swearing to "fix you up like you fixed me." He was taken back to the state institution, never to return to his family or the community.

No one likes to dwell on sorrow and misfortune.

Whenever I get to thinking about some of these sad cases I take an antidote of some kind. One of my antidotes is the case of Jules Bledsoe.

His full name was Julius C. Bledsoe. He was born in 1898 and died in 1943. He was a Negro baritone in opera, musical comedy and concert. He gained fame for his rendition of "Ol' Man River," in *Show Boat* with the Ziegfeld Company, and he appeared in the title role of *The Emperor Jones* in Europe and America.

This great Negro singer was born of humble parents

right here in Waco. He was reared by an aunt who was a teacher in the high school system here.

On one occasion, while Jules was a boy, their family doctor called me in. Jules was critically ill. The diagnosis showed a ruptured, gangrenous appendix. He was taken to the hospital and operated on immediately.

He was the most frightened little boy I have ever seen. He said, "Doctor, don't let me die; I don't want to die."

I said, "Jules, you will get well; the Lord has something for you to do!"

That seemed to have the desired effect, and thereafter I reminded him several times: "Remember what I told you—the Lord is not going to let you die; He has something for you to do."

After a tedious convalescence Jules got well.

Years afterwards he sang in Waco Hall, at Baylor University. Mrs. Crosthwait and I had front-row seats. When he came on the stage he spotted us and it seemed that he sang directly to us. There were "Ol' Man River," "Shortenin' Bread," and then the classics.

When the program was over, Jules said to me, "For a long time I have wanted to tell you what you did for me."

I told him that I recalled his appendicitis case and that it was just run-of-the-mill.

"It wasn't what you did, but what you said," he explained. "You said I would get well because the Lord had something for me to do. After I got well I began to think about what you had said, and I tried to think what He might want me to do.

"I tried several things. I wanted to be a doctor like you. Then I found out that I could sing. From that time on every hour of my wakeful time was spent in trying to improve my voice. What I am I owe to the assurance you gave me that the Lord had something for me to do."

It was a modest fee the family had paid me for the appendectomy, but I felt repaid a thousand times.

Jules died young, forty-four, at the peak of his career, and was brought back here from Hollywood for the funeral, participated in by whites and Negroes. His talent had entertained millions. And many a time since then I have drawn solace and courage from his career.

Of course, a doctor has to pay some attention to the money side of his practice, too. Sometimes, especially before the days of health insurance and charity hospitals, the circumstances of his patient were such that the fee had to be small. And in some cases, there was slow pay, or no pay at all. I'll tell you of one case where I collected johnny-on-the-spot by cutting my surgical fee out of the patient's belly.

You know there used to be cotton pickers who followed the harvest from the tip o' Texas as far north as cotton grew. I don't mean strippers, such as you have now, but honest-to-goodness cotton pickers whose nimble and dexterous fingers extracted every lock of cotton from the boll. These days the strippers and the machines snatch off the hulls and all. Real cotton picking is almost obsolete.

But I was going to say, the cotton pickers, moving from south to north as the cotton season advanced, usually had some camp followers. Many of these hangers-on were gamblers. Come payday on Saturday the gamblers would inveigle the cotton pickers into gambling and soon they would have all, or most of their pay.

Once there was a group of Mexican cotton pickers encamped about ten miles east of here (Waco). Pedro was a city-slicker Mexican here in town. He had a fine bay pony.

On payday he rode out to the country Mexicans. He got all of their money. Probably a crooked deck of cards. Pedro got on his horse and started a leisurely ride back to town, on this crisp autumn night.

One of the Mexican boys in that camp had a good horse, too. He mounted, and overtook Pedro. I guess the country Mexicans had held a council of war after they had been rooked out of their week's earnings.

Anyway, the boy caught up with Pedro, pulled out a .45-caliber pistol, and let him have it in the right side of the belly.

Dr. W. L. Souther, a Waco physician, had Pedro brought into the hospital where I was called on to operate. There was a hole as big as your fist.

The bullet had ripped away part of the appendix and I cut the rest of it out. The nurse was cleaning up in there and she came up with a wad of stuff. She looked at it and exclaimed, "Why, Doctor, that looks like money!"

I was pretty busy and we just tossed it aside on the operating table.

After we got Pedro sewed up we looked at the stuff we had taken out of him. That .45-caliber bullet looked like a mocking-bird egg in a little green nest. We cleaned up the nest and it turned out to be three $50 bills.

Those bills had gone through a lot and they were a little the worse for wear. But I took them down to the First National Bank and said, "Carl, are these any good?"

The banker looked them over and said, "Three genuine $50 bills are worth $150."

He handed me three new bills of the same denomination and he sent the old bills to the U. S. Treasury for redemption.

I said, "Carl, I cut these out of a fellow's belly and that's probably all I'll ever get out of him in the way of a fee, so I'm going to keep them."

The next day, when Pedro was on the mend, I asked him whether he had any money on him when he was shot.

He said yes, he had three $50 bills, all folded and wadded into a square of about one and a half inches. Pedro explained that he had tucked the currency into the watch pocket of his pants. An examination of the clothing showed the bullet went through a leather jacket Pedro was wearing, and then through the watch pocket, scoring a bull's-eye on the wad of bills. But there still was enough force to that bullet, fired at close range, to carry those bills right along with it, through Pedro's tough hide and into his innards.

Like all doctors, I've run across some "bad-pay" patients, but Pedro had paid.

And Pedro got a bargain out of it. He not only got the bullet and that filthy lucre removed from his system, but he got a free appendicitis operation to boot.

Not all my shooting patients lived happily ever after. Some of them died. One of them was a state banking commissioner.

This happened in East Texas. A bank got a bad report from one of the state banking examiners. The state banking commissioner made a personal inspection of the bank. After checking over the accounts he told the bank officers and some of the directors that he would have to close the bank.

The commissioner walked out on the sidewalk, locked the door and started to tack the official notice of closure on the door. The aged president of the bank suddenly drew a .45 and shot the commissioner through the chest.

That happened in the late afternoon. Two hours later

the governor telephoned me to go immediately and take charge of the victim; the commissioner was a personal friend of the governor, as well as a high-ranking state employe. I considered it a high compliment to my professional standing that the governor, whom I opposed politically, called me to succor his friend, the commissioner.

I rented a car with driver: $40 for the seventy-mile trip. My young son, who already was showing an interest in medicine, went along. There were only wagon roads from Waco to the scene of the shooting. But the chauffeur, an old cowhand, knew his business. It was a clear night, and we kept our due-east direction by the stars. We arrived about eleven p. m.

We found our patient on a cot in an upstairs room near the bank. A lone attendant told me that the local doctor had given him a shot and left word for me to take charge. It also was suggested that I get the patient out of town. The reason soon became obvious; sentiment was strongly against the state official who had "meddled" in local affairs. My thought was to get him to a hospital in Waco.

But I didn't see how he could stand the trip in the car. Besides, I discovered the auto had two flats, engine trouble and no lights. So I dismissed the driver and the car.

The town was on a junction point of the railroad. I telephoned the governor, gave him a report on the patient's condition, told him of our auto troubles and of the undesirability of moving the patient by car. I asked him to use his influence to get a special train. It developed that the company had engines available, but no baggage car and no coach. But there was a passenger train due from the opposite direction in which we wanted to travel. After much talk between Austin and Dallas, they cut a combination baggage-chair car from the passenger train, hooked it onto a special engine, and we were ready to go.

But there was another minor hitch. The owner of the iron cot wanted $5 for it, without sheet, pillow or blanket. So I paid the $5 in order to get my patient out of hock in this hostile town.

We hoisted him, cot and all, into the baggage coach. It was daylight the next morning before we arrived at the hospital, where every possible attention was given him. I remained with the patient all day, waging a losing fight. He died about midnight.

The grand jury, in session at the time of the shooting, returned a murder indictment when the man died. The accused man, because of his age, got off with a short sentence.

For my services, I was paid by the state from funds allotted to the detection and apprehension of criminals. My $5 investment in the worn-out iron cot was a total loss.

I was not doing badly, though. I found I could afford a combination receptionist-secretary. I had an automobile and a chauffeur. Trips to clinics and medical society meetings no longer were financial sacrifices. We had a comfortable home, and, incidentally, we've lived in the same house forty-four years now. We had servants. Our two children had the advantage of good schools. A great Baptist institution, Baylor University, was at our doorstep, practically. Waco offered many cultural and social benefits. The Baylor medical department, however, was situated in Dallas, about eighty-five miles north of Waco.

We've never hesitated about putting "big D" in its place; after all, we had a skyscraper before they did. But I forsook local pride to journey to Dallas frequently. For three years beginning in 1913 I lectured there before the Baylor medical department. For these fortnightly lectures I traveled between Waco and Dallas on the interurban, an electric line which was abandoned later, when autos came into general use. There was no pay in it for me, just the privilege of being a professor again. There was personal satisfaction later when my son graduated from the Baylor Medical School, and in the school year of 1955–56 my grandson, Robert Crosthwait, was in his first year of medical school at Baylor.

During my early years in Waco I was secretary of the State Board of Medical Examiners. This was an eleven-member board appointed by the governor. The board had rather broad powers. These included the examination of graduates in medicine and surgery, passing on applicants for licenses under a reciprocity agreement among the states, the inspection of medical colleges and their classification in cooperation with the American Medical Association and later with the American College of Surgeons.

As secretary of the state board I was kept busy. It meant long hours, a vast correspondence and frequent trips to inspect colleges and attend board meetings. All of that, however, had its compensations. I got acquainted with many doctors, teachers and trustees. It afforded a wonderful opportunity to keep up with the progress of medical education.

Each year we held three-day examinations for graduates of medical schools who desired to practice medicine or surgery in Texas.

I have mentioned my experience in instituting an honor system in the backwoods school of Mississippi. I was disappointed when a similar system failed in Texas. The medical examinations were held in a large hall, usually the House of Representatives at the capitol where the desks of the legislators were a perfect setup for cheaters.

Each examiner brought his questions, which had been printed in his home town. On more than one occasion some enterprising student went to the local printer, got copies of the questions and peddled these to his mates.

We broke that up by getting a mimeograph outfit and mimeographing the questions on the spot.

But we still had the so-called point system to deal with. That was simply looking in the book and getting the answers to the questions. We didn't want to expose and disgrace any of our boys. So we devised a very effective scheme.

We had an applicant from another state, a stranger to our Texas applicants, who was entitled to a license by reciprocity, but his credentials had not been fully verified. We proceeded to seek verification by wire while he began a written examination with the boys. By noon we had verified his status as a doctor, and we called him to our executive meeting. He already had observed that cheating was going on, so he agreed to play along with us. He started the afternoon exam with a pony and a pocketful of notes. As planned, he was caught by one of our examiners and literally dragged up to the secretary's desk where he was given a tongue lashing and then shoved out of the hall.

There was an exodus to the washroom to dispose of ponies and notes, and there was no more cheating.

Medical colleges were being standardized in Texas and all over the nation. The entrance requirements were increased from a high school diploma (fourteen Carnegie units) to two full college years, and some medical schools began to insist upon a B.A. or B.S. degree as a prerequisite.

Medical schools were classed as A, B, or C. Students from class C schools were unacceptable to our board of examiners and to most of the examining boards of the nation.

The B schools were placed on limited probation. The result was that the B and C medical schools either merged with class A schools or closed up. That was the end of the diploma mills.

I am glad that I had some part in elevating the standard of medical education.

And this, I repeat, was the indirect result of my dabbling in politics.

To be sure, when a doctor does that he opens himself to criticism by those who misunderstand his motives. Also he becomes fair game in the rough-and-tumble contests of politicians. I had fared well under the administrations of Governors S. W. T. Lanham (1903–07), Thomas M. Campbell (1907–11) and O. B. Colquitt (1911–15).

When "Farmer Jim" Ferguson became governor in 1915 I was not an applicant for reappointment as secretary of the State Board of Medical Examiners. Years previously he had told a Democratic convention that I didn't "know nothing" about legislation, but we were still friends. Jim was a Bell County man, practically a neighbor of mine in the Holland area, but he and I never did see eye-to-eye politically. Old Jim is dead and gone now, and I don't intend to review his political career. I'll say this, though: Even though we were political foes, Jim called on me for professional services whenever it was expedient.

Even if I had been a candidate for reappointment and even if Jim had been of a mind to take me into his official family, I doubt that I could have given the job the attention that I thought it should have. My practice, especially my surgical activity, had increased to the point where I could not afford even a part-time political position.

Sometimes I think that the period around 1912–13 was

a golden age for a great many of us. Except for the Balkan wars, the world was pretty much at peace. The great powers of Europe had not warred among themselves for more than forty years. In the wake of the Spanish-American War the United States was building a great nation by a natural increase in population plus the absorption of surplus population from other countries. In the South most of the vestiges of reconstruction days were wiped out. Gasoline and electricity were making for the good life.

The aristocracy of slavery days had gone with the wind, but a new aristocracy built on cotton, cattle and oil was coming into being.

In 1914 a political fanatic assassinated Archduke Francis Ferdinand, heir to the throne of Austria-Hungary, and Europe was plunged into war. Three years later we were in it.

OFF TO THE WAR

WHEN A state of war was declared with Germany and the Central Powers, the government announced a need for doctors. That was April, 1917.

At the breakfast table we held our own council of war. Even though it would mean many readjustments in our affairs, my wife and children voted in favor of my volunteering my services. My son, then thirteen, was going to be a doctor, too. The family vote decided the question. I wired the surgeon-general's office that I was available.

I was told that if I was given a major's commission I might be assigned paper work. I didn't want a swivel chair. I wanted active, front-line duty, if possible. The best chance for that seemed to be to accept the lower rank of captain.

On my forty-fourth birthday, May 2, 1917, I took my examinations in Dallas, and on June 28, 1917, I was commissioned a captain in the medical section of the Officers Reserve Corps. I thought of that fat, little captain who turned me down in 1899 and told me an ocean crossing would kill me. I wonder whether he's still living.

While I got a certain satisfaction out of Uncle's earmarking me for foreign service almost twenty years later, there were other things that served as a bit of a damper to my enthusiasm. Some of my insurance policies carried a clause that canceled the benefits if I met death in a war zone. By that time, I suppose, I was grossing $25,000 a year in private practice. My captain's pay and allowances amounted to about $2,500, and the comedown meant some changes in our household. While I was waiting for orders Mrs. Crosthwait had to have an appendicitis operation.

In December of that year I was ordered to report to the University of Chicago for a four-months intensive course in the U. S. Neurosurgical School. The trip was a reminder to me of at least two previous journeys to the same city, one the pre-hurricane voyage of 1900 and the other, some years later, when I sought out a cadaver with a goiter.

But at the neurosurgical school, the first of its kind in this country, there was no time for looking back. We were off to new adventures in anatomy, physiology, pathology and surgery. Our faculty was composed of some of the leading lights in medical and surgical practice, and in medical education.

Among those who took the course was Dr. Evarts A. Graham, St. Louis, who became president of the International Congress of Surgeons and who holds the Distinguished Service Medal of the American Medical Association. In France he served as commanding officer of Evacuation Hospital No. 34.

After completing the course I was sent back to Camp McArthur at Waco, and then was assigned to Base Hospital No. 55, a Massachusetts General Hospital unit marked for overseas duty. In July, 1918, we mobilized at Camp Greenleaf, Georgia. Most of our three weeks there was spent in lectures and in drills in defense against gas. The unit was composed largely of Harvard University men, and they were a fine bunch. I may have been the only non-Harvard man in the outfit. The group was known as one of the Cushing teams, named in honor of the great surgeon, Dr. Harvey Cushing, whose techniques I had admired and tried to emulate.

One afternoon I took a stroll about the countryside near the camp. I turned down a lane by the side of a small farm. There were rows of peach trees and in between the trees there were rows of peanuts, better known in the South at that time as "goobers."

There was a white-haired colored gentleman hoeing out the weeds. I engaged him in conversation. There happened to be an airplane circling overhead. The old colored man kept looking up at it, rather apprehensively, I thought.

I said, "Uncle, how would you like to be up in that airplane?"

He said, "No, sah, I never wants to be higher than picking peaches and no lower than grabbling goobers."

I thought it was a fine bit of local color, and that evening I told the story in the officers' mess. It was received in polite silence.

I explained that in the South peanuts were called goobers, a word possibly of west African origin. The word "grabble" is a good old English word, probably derived from the Dutch "grabbelen." It means probing with your fingers for the first fruits of a tuberous plant. In the South it came to mean the harvesting by hand of early potatoes or early peanuts without injuring the roots or the younger fruits. That way you could have new potatoes very early.

But by the time I went into these details the story itself was lost.

I don't hear you laughing, either.

While we were in the Georgia camp a group of us made an excursion to the battlefield of Chickamauga. Someone pointed out the site of Brotherton House, where my grandfather took refuge fifty-five years previously, after he had been wounded by the damyankees.

I had a nightmarish thought. Suppose Grandpa's spirit haunted the battlefield and he should see me hobnobbing with the descendants of his enemies.

But those Northern fellows and I got along famously. We were shipped from Georgia to Camp Dix, then to embarkation at Alpine Landing, Weehawken, New Jersey, on August 29. Our ship was the U.S. transport *Plattsburg*, formerly the S.S. *New York*. There were German submarines lurking in North Atlantic waters, but we didn't see any. I remember one little incident, though. One of our young lieutenants fell violently and overwhelmingly in love with one of our nurses. It appeared to be mutual. Our convoy of fifteen ships ran into a five-day storm and everyone got seasick, including the lovebirds. There are all kinds of complications in human affairs, of course, but I don't believe there is anything worse than a combination of seasickness and lovesickness. We landed at Brest, France, after an eighteen-day voyage and I became too busy to keep up with the progress of that romance.

We were sent to Orleans; then to Tours, on the Loire, thence to the Toul sector, on the Moselle, where we arrived September 28. We were near St. Mihiel and Argonne Wood. The St. Mihiel offensive had passed into history. Between the Argonne forest and the Meuse and between the Meuse and the Moselle the Germans were staging fierce counterattacks, but on the verge of final retreat. Air battles raged behind the lines.

In addition to some 2,000 Allied and enemy wounded who arrive at our hospital each day, we had some victims of gas gangrene. This was caused by the Welch bacillus in wounds contaminated by filth, feces, etc., on the fighting terrain. The victims of this battlefield hazard almost invariably were Americans. At least none of the Heinies who fell into our hands as captives were thus afflicted. I could not understand why they seemed to be immune.

I still have a list of soldiers—Americans, and German prisoners of war—on whom I operated during the closing months of war. I have their names, their military units, whence they came, and, in some cases, their home addresses. I wonder how many are in the land of the living.

Many Americans were sick with influenza—Spanish influenza, we called it. There were many fatalities. This loss was to be expected. Frequently a germ that hits you in foreign fields is more potent than the same kind of germ hitting you at home base. Or, let's put it this way: Abroad you run into germs to which your system has not built up a resistance.

I picked up the bug and was down for a few weeks. I got up just in time to catch a whiff of phosgene gas. By that time the war was drawing to a close, and the retreating German Army was using that stuff to protect their rear. The cough I have had since childhood was aggravated by the gas, but peace was on the horizon.

I well remember the fateful hour of eleven a. m. on November 11, 1918. The waiting room outside our operating rooms in France was filled with wounded American and allied soldiers. As the clock struck eleven a. m. I raised the dark curtains which had shut out the light from the view of enemy planes. In the village were shouts of, "La guerre est finie." At that moment, the sun, which had been obscured by clouds that hung thick and low over the countryside, broke through. The bright sunshine fell upon a cross, which had been kept in hiding. When peace came, the cross quickly was replaced on the village church. The cross had been freshly painted in gold, and to me it seemed that the reflected rays of the sun were a message of hope for a peaceful world and a better life for all liberty-loving peoples.

After the armistice I became friendly with a German captain who was among my wounded prisoners, and I asked him just how the Germans had escaped gas gangrene. He explained they had been inoculated with anti-gas-gangrene vaccine. That was something we did not have at that time; if we had had the vaccine many lives and limbs might have been saved.

My operating team of two surgeons, two nurses and two corps boys was sent on various missions. There were times when no messes were available and we had no provisions with us. One occasion I recall particularly. We had been traveling all day over narrow-gauge rail lines, with many detours due to blasted trackage. We wound up about midnight in Bar-le-Duc. We were hungry and we talked the guards into letting us through to the hôtel de ville (city hall). In a great banquet hall in the basement, there was a feast in progress. The mayor and other high-ranking officials and officers were there in striped pants, scissor-tailed coats and fancy uniforms. Great platters of meat were making the rounds.

We sat down at a nearby table, and told the madame we wanted meat. She threw up her hands in a gesture to indicate there was no meat.

"What are those fellows eating over there?" we wanted to know.

That was too much English for madame. She went over and whispered and gesticulated to the mayor.

His Honor came over to our table, bowed and scraped, and said, "Zee madame hesitates to offer zee Americaine officers zee horsemeat."

We told the mayor to bring on the horsemeat, and he had it served with a salutation of, "zee bon appetit."

Zat was my first bite of horsemeat. I ate it, but I did not relish it. Memories of my days as a horseback doctor seemed to haunt my palate.

Since World War II there have been stories about the destruction of government surplus. The same thing happened after World War I. I saw several cases of brain-surgery instruments, each of them valued at more than $1,000, thrown on a dump. All during my tour of duty I had wanted some of those particular instruments. I took one case from a dump to the hospital. After the armistice I talked to the commanding officer to see whether I couldn't keep it. He said the government had a contract with the manufacturer not to return any of them to civilian trade. "But," he added, "if you want one you just have to steal it." I didn't sleep well that night, and the next morning I returned the case of instruments to the dump. There it and other surplus material were blasted into uselessness.

About three months after the armistice I was ordered to take a bunch of casualties from Saverne, near Strasbourg, to Brest for departure home. It was an all-night trip on a special train, and I had several very sick boys in my group. One of them required my attention most of the time while the train clackety-clacked across France. He told me he hoped to live at least until he got one more glimpse of the Statue of Liberty.

Troop train No. 61 arrived in Brest on the morning of February 1, 1919. I remember the train and date because they were of particular importance to me. I had been tipped off that General John J. Pershing himself might be at the port of embarkation. I made a tour of the train and had a sergeant police each car. There had been reports that some trains had been coming in there in bad sanitary condition.

When No. 61 stopped for breakfast and inspection I saw a group of officers board the train, and among them was the Commander in Chief of the American Expeditionary Force. I cowered in a corner of a car scared to death he would find something wrong. After the inspection a colonel found me, escorted me off the train and brought me face to face with Black Jack Pershing.

"I've called you out here," said the general, "to personally commend you, before my staff, for bringing this train in in first-class condition."

It would be an understatement to say I felt relieved.

We came back on the *Leviathan,* an uneventful crossing. It was a clear day when the ship approached Bedloe's Island. My sickest boy had his wish fulfilled. He was brought out on deck on a stretcher for a glimpse of the Statue of Liberty. He smiled wanly, and when they returned him to his bunk he was dead.

I was commissioned a major in the reserves, discharged, and returned to Waco to resume my practice. But there were postwar problems that demanded attention.

The Veterans Administration had not been organized. I was appointed officer in charge of the sick and wounded in my area and was given a rating as assistant surgeon in the

U. S. Public Health Service. My salary was $100 per month; my secretary cost me $125 a month. I served a year or so, until the Veterans Administration took over.

I was appointed to the State Board of Health by Governor W. P. Hobby (1917–21), who became governor when Jim Ferguson was ousted. My appointment by Hobby probably was through the influence of my former partner, Dr. Goddard. He had become state health officer. We discussed the needs of ex-servicemen who had been gassed, and we organized the Texas War Risk Society. I recall I paid for the charter out of my own pocket. Pat Neff, who was to become governor (1921–25), and later interstate commerce commissioner, Texas railroad commissioner and finally president of Baylor University, agreed to serve on the board.

The Schreiner family of Kerrville gave a 400-acre site and $40,000 cash. We started a building on the tract. The state department of the American Legion was organized. We turned the project over to them, along with $20,000 cash. A legion official pocketed a lot of the money and left. The legion made it good by assessing each member $10. Then the institution was turned over to the state, which, in turn, transferred it to the federal government. Today a plant worth millions is under the Veterans Administration.

We had other postwar problems besides the wounded, the gassed and the shell-shocked.

Bubonic plague showed up.

We think of this pestilence as something ancient. Josephus speaks of Black Death that overwhelmed Egypt, spreading to the ports of the Mediterranean and finally to the Adriatic coast. The great epidemic of A. D. 1334 started in China, reached Italy in 1338, and then spread to Spain, France, England and all of Europe. The estimated population of Europe at that time was around 100,000,000. Pope Clement IV estimated the total number of deaths at 42,000,000.

Scores of plague epidemics of lesser proportion have occurred throughout the world since then. With our rapid means of transportation it is not inconceivable that it could happen again. Deepwater ports always have borne the brunt of the attacks; great international airports of today could bring the germ far into the interior.

The disease appeared in Galveston on June 16, 1920. It was reported to the state health officer in Austin, Texas, at eleven p. m. that date. As a member of the State Board of Health I was notified a few minutes later. I caught a midnight train to Houston where I met the state health officer. Dr. Goddard and I proceeded to Galveston. There, in collaboration with the faculty of the medical department of the University of Texas and with the use of their laboratory, the diagnosis of bubonic plague was established beyond the shadow of a doubt, by noon of June 17. The case resulted in death within a few hours.

I recalled the hurricane of 1900 and how it took many lives on this island in a matter of a few hours. Was a disastrous epidemic about to strike?

At Beaumont, on June 19, the first victim was an employe at a warehouse where rat-infested hay, taken off a vessel from an infected port, was stored. Another patient was a housewife who lived near the wharves and who had been bitten while trying to kill rats. It is probable that the infected rat came in on a ship from some port along the Mexican coast.

It was around Juneteenth (Negro Emancipation Day in Texas) that a Negro boy in a suburb of Beaumont was stricken. He suffered violent pains in his stomach, vomiting, rigors and fever, shortly after eating a hot dog at a local joint. A Negro doctor was called. He diagnosed the case as acute indigestion. This doctor called on the keeper of the joint and demanded payment for treatment of the boy, claiming that the hot dog had caused the trouble. The hot-dog man called another Negro doctor, who concurred in the first diagnosis. Both these doctors demanded fees from the hot-dog merchant. In the meantime, the family called in a third Negro doctor, who signed the death certificate —"death due to acute indigestion."

Our plague commissioner, Dr. H. C. Hall, was examining all burial permits. When he noted that this death occurred within eight hours after onset and that the victim was a young Negro boy (probably with a digestive system that could handle one little old hot dog even on Juneteenth), Dr. Hall suspected plague. He had the body exhumed and examined. A positive diagnosis of plague resulted.

The first case in Houston, first diagnosed as acute appendicitis, brought death in a few hours.

There were some twenty-four cases of plague in Texas at that time, including one of the most dreaded, the pneumonic type. This type made the situation far more serious because the infection spread from person to person by the droplet method, quite similar to the spread of influenza.

Of the several kinds of rats in Texas, the Norway rat, prevalent on wharves and in cellars and barns, was found to be infected. Most infected rats died near their habitat, but during the incubation period of from one to seven days, they traveled quite a distance. A few rats probably outlived the disease and became carriers. In addition, fleas from infected rats became carriers.

This is the way it works:

As soon as the flea gets the bacillus (Pasteurella pestis bubonicae) in his stomach he begins to incubate it. The bacilli multiply in great numbers. His stomach becomes distended and his intestinal tract becomes clogged. The fleas vomit; some have diarrhea. When such a flea bites a human being he sucks up the blood and the peristaltic action of the stomach is like a bellows, which pumps the blood back into the person, thus carrying the bacilli into the human system. If the flea happens to be one of the diarrhea type he usually makes an abrasion and smears it over with flea feces. And when the person begins to scratch the itchy spot he may be scratching his name off the list of mortals.

We have not had a major epidemic of bubonic plague to test some of the newer drugs. U. S. Naval researchers have reported that one of the antibiotics, streptomycin, was effective in experimental bubonic and pneumonic plague in mice and guinea pigs. A doctor in India reported that in an outbreak of bubonic plague there in January, 1953, there were eighteen cases and all cases were cured with streptomycin.

By far the most desirable approach to the problem is control. These measures consist of ratproofing buildings, wharves and piers; fumigating likely habitations of rats; starving rats by keeping food out of their reach, and by trapping, shooting and poisoning the rodents.

In Texas we ratproofed all the ports from Beaumont to Galveston, killed thousands of rats and segregated all suspected cases of plague. The cost was a few thousand dollars.

Had the epidemic been permitted to spread, it would have cost the state many millions of dollars, not to mention the loss of life.

It was high time for me to resume my private practice in an effort to recoup financially.

The mid-'20s were prosperous years. The slogan of the U. S. Chamber of Commerce was, "Nothing can stop us now." American goals were two cars in every garage and two chickens in every pot. Many collegians, possibly the fathers of today's panty raiders, were swallowing goldfish. Herring would have been cheaper, but we were living in the gilt-edged '20s.

I've been trying to give you dates, as well as I can recall them, but they don't mean much unless you get the flavor of the times.

Remember that in the mid-'20s ex-Kaiser Wilhelm was sawing cordwood, President Coolidge was riding a private hobbyhorse for exercise, and the world was laughing at the Prince of Wales for repeatedly falling off his horse. Magda Lupescu had pernicious anemia and was about to have King Carol of Rumania. "Ma" Ferguson was governor of Texas. ("Two governors for the price of one," Jim had told the electorate, and I went to the political doghouse.) The Four Horsemen of Notre Dame were riding into football fame. A schoolteacher in Tennessee was convicted and fined $100 after a sensational trial on a charge of teaching the theory of evolution. The Ku Klux Klan was in its heyday. Floyd Collins, trapped in a Kentucky cave, held public interest for weeks, until he was found dead. Tallulah Bankhead was wowing 'em in Europe, and back home we had Gilda Grey, the shimmy queen, and Clara Bow, the "It" girl. Some couples were trying companionate marriage and some churches were dropping "obey" from the marriage vows. There was prohibition, and the rum fleet was anchored just beyond the three-mile limit.

A typical vaudeville joke, over the telephone, was:

"Say, we've got a girl here with a case of laryngitis."

"Bring it right over, these guys will drink anything."

It became fashionable to have your appendix taken out. Folks might laugh when you sat down at the piano, but if you could yank up your shirt and show an operation scar you were not a social outcast.

I don't mean to say that such operations were not necessary in many cases. I speak from experience.

It was a warm summer night, in the late '20s, I suppose. With some visitors and my family I had been sitting out on the front lawn trying to catch what little breeze there was.

I had eaten a very light supper. That was before we got high-hat and started calling it "dinner." About ten p. m. I began to be nauseated. I went into the house, undressed, and put on my pajamas. The visitors and the family retired. I went back out on the lawn. The pain began in the upper abdomen, then circled about the umbilicus. The nausea got worse and the pain began to localize in the lower right quadrant, and a chilly fever came over me.

I knew then that I had appendicitis. I walked over to the hospital, three blocks away, and told the night sister to get ready for an operation for acute appendicitis. I had the house doctor give me a sedative as the pain was quite severe. I ordered a blood count on myself just for the record. I then went up to surgery and asked what table I should use. I crawled up on the table.

The head nurse, who had been out while all this was going on, came in, looked at me reprovingly and said, "Now, look, Doctor, this is for the patient!"

She talked to me as if I was a dog in the manger.

I said, "I am the patient. Hurry and get me a surgeon quick!"

My son and his father-in-law, the late Dr. K. H. Aynesworth, who was a distinguished surgeon, came charging in. They said, "How do you know you have appendicitis?"

I grumbled, "If you felt as I do, you would know that you had it. Get ready and get it out."

A gangrenous appendix was removed, just minutes before it might have ruptured. In those days a ruptured appendix was serious indeed.

I made a good recovery, thanks to my son and Dr. Aynesworth.

Then I was ready again to do the same for others. One of my first patients was my barber. I like barbers. You can sit down in a barber chair and your barber will talk to you about the things you like to hear. They use a certain psychology. My barber knew I was the football-team physician and when I came into his shop he knew exactly what to talk about.

Sometimes his razor would nick me a little, and I would kid him. I'd say, "Now, Bob, you stick to your barbering and let me do the surgery. It has been a long time since barbers had license to do bloodletting."

One forenoon while I was operating, my barber was wheeled into surgery for an appendectomy. I took full advantage of the situation. In those days doctors sharpened their own knives and scissors. I walked into the operating room whetting my scalpel. You wouldn't think that a little thing like that would bother a man who used a razor on other folks, would you?

But my barber, wall-eyed as I vigorously sharpened my instrument, looked up at me and said, "Doctor, please go easy on me for I am awfully easy killed."

In the long run, he proved hard to kill in a hospital. The next morning, on my visiting rounds, I found him standing up before the dresser mirror and shaving himself with a straight-edge razor. That was before the days of early ambulation and I thought, "Old boy, if you are so easy killed you had better get back on the bed and stay there!" But he was up and around every day until he was discharged. Some months later he was killed in an auto wreck.

But, speaking of operations, especially appendicitis operations, there is a school of thought nowadays that holds that the patient should move about shortly after surgery. There is merit in the idea, but it can be overdone. I should say that it would depend entirely upon the individual case.

I recall a story I heard recently. The doctor on the case was convinced that his patient should get back into circulation immediately after the operation. So, just before surgery, the doctor told his patient that within a few hours he expected him to sit up in bed; in a few more hours he was to stand up, then walk around, and in a couple of days he was to take long walks.

The patient took it all in, mulled it over, and said, "Doctor, would it be all right with you if I lie down for the operation?"

The roaring '20s came to a grinding halt. I don't intend to review the great depression, or my own losses. Obviously when the general economy was in the doldrums the doctor had poor sailing. There were not as many imaginary ills, and a large percentage of the bona-fide cases was charity.

All kinds of fancy names have been applied to these periods in our economic history. They call them deflations, depressions, panics, crises and cycles. We called them "hard times." They seemed to come with some degree of regularity.

I was born in the midst of worldwide hard times in 1873. When I was ten we had another period of stress. When I was twenty and struggling to get started, the depression of 1893 seized most of the nation. Money was tight when I was thirty, and hard times hit again at thirty-five. When I was forty-two the price of cotton went 'way down, and many of my patients could not pay. And in 1929, when I was fifty-six, we really had a humdinger that ran well up into the 1930s. It was too recent and too painful to dwell on now.

It was during this period that I again lectured at Baylor University, this time in Waco. My subject was medical jurisprudence. Before the war I had lectured in Dallas before students who were going into medicine; now I was lecturing before those going into law as well as pre-medical students.

Baylor was one of the few law schools in the country that had a department of medical jurisprudence at that time. The relationship of the two great professions, law and medicine, has always interested me.

I undertook to tell medical students how, as doctors, they must conduct themselves when called as witnesses; what a doctor's legal rights are with respect to maintaining the confidential relationship between patient and doctor; what a doctor's obligations are in reporting violent death, quarantinable diseases and vital statistics, and how a doctor can defend himself in the event of damage suit in connection with medical or surgical treatment.

The would-be lawyers I gave a briefing in medicine so that they might ask intelligent questions in eliciting medical testimony; some anatomical and surgical pointers in personal-injury suits; ways of spotting the malingerer and the make-believe psychopath, and how medical science can aid in the detection and prosecution of criminals.

There was no pay for my lectures, but there was a certain self-satisfaction. In a way, I was completing a cycle in my own career, from "professor" in a one-room rural school in Mississippi to professor of medical jurisprudence at a great institution of higher learning in Texas.

One day a student said to me, "Professor, the depression is over." I said, "How do you know?"

He said, "Well, I saw a rabbit run across the campus and there was no one after him."

The end of hard times was not that sudden. As it had started, the depression wound up in a crazy-quilt of recovery. But once we got started again, nothing could stop us. Doctors, ethical and otherwise, found their practice flourishing.

A notorious case in Texas at the time was a goat-gland doctor. He set up practice in the goat-raising country of west Texas and advertised by radio and press that he could rejuvenate males by grafting goat glands into their loins. Many men of wealth who had passed their sexual prime journeyed to the arid west to find the fountain of youth. Goat glands were expensive and ineffectual. The American Medical Association fought the practice through the courts until death closed the career of the charlatan.

The 1930s were busy years for me. My office hours and my hospital operations became more or less systematized.

They became a routine of punctuality and precision, far removed from horseback and horse-and-buggy practice. My son, Robert Wilson Crosthwait, was graduated from Baylor University Medical School; served his internship at Harpers Hospital, Detroit, and held a fellowship at the University of Pennsylvania Hospital. He returned to Waco and became a full partner of mine.

We were operating at two hospitals, which had become training schools for nurses and interns. I was chief of staff at different times as well as chief of neurosurgery at both hospitals (total 500 beds). For many years I lectured to classes in both hospitals.

Literally speaking, I came down in the world. I moved from the skyscraper, which years previously had beckoned me to Waco, and established a clinic on a ground-floor location.

I was becoming stout and I decided I needed a hobby that would give me exercise. I tried golf, played a few games, made some good shots accidentally, and got the idea I might be a pretty good golfer. All I needed was some good pointers. I took lessons from a pro, and promptly slipped from the low 80s to the high 90s. It's a wonder the pro didn't throw a club at me.

I quit golf and fell back on football, my first love, but not as a player, I hasten to add. For thirty-five years I served as team physician for the Waco High School Tigers, who became famous in state prep ranks under the late Coach Paul L. Tyson. When my golf soured on me I became a stronger rooter than ever for our football team.

In passing I would add that football has developed from its rough-and-tumble beginnings to a game of science, precision, skill, art, exact timing, speed, power, and, above all, loyalty and confidence. Because they are builders of character, our conscientious coaches are due a debt of gratitude which we can never repay.

There are many injuries, to be sure. I have treated all kinds, but the benefits of the game outweigh the drawbacks.

The Duke of Wellington, whose troops vanquished Napoleon's forces, said the Battle of Waterloo was won on the playing fields of Eton. General Douglas MacArthur, when he was superintendent of the U. S. Military Academy, put it this way: "On the fields of friendly strife are sown the seeds which in other fields bear the fruits of victory."

Golf or no, I felt I had kept myself in pretty good condition, and I volunteered when World War II came along.

They said I was too old. I was sixty-eight. I thought of the little captain who had turned me down in 1899 because he thought an ocean crossing would kill me.

If and when World War III comes along I suppose some little whippersnapper will tell me I am too old for service or that I won't survive an ocean crossing.

I have traveled a lot even since World War II. Mrs. Doctor, who assisted me during my horse-and-buggy days, almost always was with me whether we traveled by auto, rail or air. She also made two trips to Europe with the children. In September, 1950, on our way back from a meeting of the American College of Surgeons in New York City, she survived a heart attack.

THE HELPING HAND

BEFORE I have done with my story I want to insert a card of thanks. It is addressed to all who have helped me attain my life's ambition. No man is sufficient unto himself.

A wise man is wise because he has sense enough to listen to the voice of experience. The reason a fool is not wise is because he does not have that much sense.

I feel I have been fortunate indeed in coming in contact with some of the greatest American physicians and surgeons of my time. I learned a great deal from them. As a country doctor I felt that I was in the company of the great. Sometimes I had to subdue a certain timidity. I would like to add here that I have found that the greater a man is, the more approachable he is likely to be. I have the impression that some of our younger doctors, especially those in smaller communities, do not fully appreciate this fact. In consequence, they hesitate to approach the famous physician or surgeon, and they are robbing themselves—and their patients—of the benefit of experienced guidance.

I have lived long enough—and have screwed up my courage enough—to have become acquainted with three generations of the Mayos. The elder Dr. William W. Mayo was one of the most interesting of characters. After the turn of the century I often visited the Mayos at Rochester, Minnesota, and I had many talks with the fine old doctor. He had been sent there many years previously as a medical officer to look after the Indians. He told me of northern blizzards, of a cyclone which destroyed the village of Rochester, of his relief work there, and of the subsequent establishment of a hospital by the Sisters of Charity, now known as St. Mary's. He was appointed chief of staff, and the Mayos have served in that capacity to this good hour.

The Mayo brothers, Will and Charlie, were the co-founders of the Mayo Clinic, probably the greatest in the world and certainly the pattern for hundreds of other clinics throughout the country. They were not only great surgeons, but also fine teachers and good hosts. They used to invite visiting doctors out to their homes for dinner one evening a week. I had the honor of being their guest on several occasions.

Among others I knew was the great John B. Murphy, inventor of the Murphy button for anastomosing intestines. That was before doctors learned to sew intestines together so they would not leak. Dr. Murphy reported 1,000 appendicitis operations with a very low mortality for that time. He also originated the Murphy treatment for what they called inoperable appendicitis. This treatment supplied fluids through the rectum. It was known as the Murphy Drip and was widely used for years, until the advent of intravenous medication now in use.

I was well acquainted with Dr. Albert J. Ochner, chief surgeon at the Augustana Hospital, Chicago. He originated a treatment like the Murphy Drip, with some valuable additions to take care of patients with peritonitis from ruptured, gangrenous appendixes and from other causes. The

Ochner treatment saved many lives during the days when there were few competent surgeons.

In Chicago also I came to know Dr. Hugh Ferguson, who had a small hospital on the North Side. He originated Ferguson's modification of the Basini operation for hernia. I learned a lot from him and felt very appreciative.

I have told how I saw Dr. Wyeth, the great New York surgeon, spot a man's hernia without examination; how I was so impressed that our honeymoon trip had to make way for a postgraduate course.

There is an old Chinese proverb: A skilled physician knows from observation, a mediocre doctor from interrogation and an ordinary doctor from palpation.

If you have a good doctor and he says, "I want to see you" on such and such a date, he doesn't mean that he just wants to pass the time of day with you. He wants to observe. Keep this in mind when it may appear to you that a telephone call would serve as well as a personal visit.

There are all kinds of tests, instruments and apparatuses to show how various organs of the body are functioning. Well and good. But I know of no contrivance that will give an over-all picture of the patient. That is where the general practitioner's powers of observation come into play.

Early in my story I mentioned a doctor, much older than I was at the time, who diagnosed a case of typhoid fever by his sense of smell. I did not mention his name, but I would like to give it now. He was Dr. John T. Harrington, a Mississippian who became chairman of the board of trustees of Baylor University.

He was serving as chairman in 1947 when Baylor decided to confer an honorary degree of L.L.D. on President Truman. It was Dr. Harrington's prerogative to present the President of the United States to the president of Baylor, but the doctor was suffering from a malignant disease and he knew his time was near. I had the honor and privilege of taking care of him. He told me he wanted to live at least until he could make the presentation.

To sustain him during the exercises I gave him a blood transfusion that morning. He carried out, with some difficulty, the crowning ambition of his life. He died soon afterward.

I could go on like this, telling about leaders who have pointed the way in my profession, but you might conclude that I was taking the columnist's stock-in-trade of name-dropping.

To all these men and to others too numerous to mention—and in many cases their names would mean nothing outside their own communities—I owe a debt which I cannot repay. It is part of my unfinished business on this earth. I suppose all of us are in a similar situation, more or less.

Among the debts I tried to repay, at least in a measure, was that to Dr. George F. Border. You will recall he was the mystery man who drifted into Holland about 1897. After a period of delirium he recovered from typhoid, and then he set up a medical practice which he turned over to me when he left for Oklahoma.

I watched his career. He was elected mayor of the town of Mangum. He got into some kind of row with the utility company that was supplying Mangum with light and power. There was a big lawsuit. The company's franchise was coming up for extension and Border's term of office was expiring. He was re-elected and the company's application for renewal of the franchise was rejected. And, Border told me, that was the beginning of Mangum's municipal utility system.

Eventually he went to Oklahoma City and opened a clinic there.

In 1951 I received a message that old George was critically ill. I went up there, but I was too late to do any good. I was at his bedside when death came. He died intestate, and I saw to it that his son, whom he had not seen in a long time, was recognized as the rightful heir. Some day I hope to write the saga of Dr. Border, my friend for more than a half century.

Now I want to digress momentarily to pay tribute to all doctors' wives, and to my wife in particular, for the valiant and unselfish part they have played under the conditions which go with their lot in life.

Once I addressed my colleagues in Texas on the topic, "The Doctor's Life, the Doctor's Wife." As I reread the speech today it seems a bit flowery in form, but the sentiment remains the same:

"If the doctor has suffered deprivations and hardships in pursuing a profession devoted to the cause of humanity, the doctor's wife has suffered infinitely more in sharing that life with him. The doctor's devotion to his calling, his deeds of heroism in times of extreme danger, his sacrifice of health and life in the name of scientific advancement—all these have been thought most fitting for the best efforts of the painter, the sculptor and the orator. But, my friends, the inimitable character, the unreserved devotion and the never-faltering fidelity of the doctor's wife cannot be portrayed upon canvas by the brush of the artist; cannot be fashioned upon inanimate stone or brass by the most gifted sculptor, nor can these qualities be recounted in the words of the world's most eloquent orator.

"Friends, the world laughs when we laugh, but weeps not when we weep. . . . It is then that the doctor's wife comes to irradiate our benighted minds with the cheering beams of truth and love and life and hope."

From time to time there have been references in these reminiscences to Mrs. Crosthwait, better known among my patients as Mrs. Doctor, my cherished wife for fifty-five years. She took an active interest in the conception and preparation of this narrative, which is dedicated to her.

Sometimes Mrs. Doctor, who had sat at the bedside of many of my patients, was in the hospital herself for medical attention. I would take my story to her, chapter by chapter as they were completed, and read it to her. And she was pleased when I read a letter from the publisher that another of our honeymoon dreams would come true, that this book would be published.

Often we recalled incidents or associations that had meant a great deal in the furtherance of my ambitions.

Another thing that has been helpful to me in my career has been medical literature, and that includes some of the popular magazines. I have not forgotten that it was from a popular magazine, rather than a medical journal, that I first learned of goiter operations.

It seems to me that medical textbooks and journals in various phases of medicine have tended to be ultraconservative in dealing with innovations. The reason is obvious and the objective is laudable. No medical writer or editor wants to lead a doctor into unfounded confidence; no doctor wants to give his patient false hope. This is why we have leaned backwards in our medical literature.

To perpetuate that policy is to assume that there has been no progress in communicating ideas. A half century ago a medical treatise on a controversial topic might have gone unchallenged for a long time. Opposing views might have to await medical conventions. Today, if you come out with a theory on the cause of cancer or if you offer a new vaccine, the pros and cons are argued immediately; at least in a succeeding issue of the newspaper, if not in the same issue.

Doctors are not as allergic to printer's ink as they once were, and the public is not as prudish about the facts of life in white and black. If there is any doubt about this, turn back to the official record of a Presidential news conference in Denver, Colorado, September 26, 1955.

President Eisenhower had been stricken with a heart attack two days previously.

At the news conference, one of his physicians, Dr. Paul Dudley White, an internationally known heart specialist, insisted upon telling the public that the President had had a good bowel movement that morning.

". . . the country will be very pleased," the specialist was quoted by the press, "and it is important."

To get back to my own career, I believe in organization. For years I've belonged to the American Medical Association, the McLennan County Medical Society and the Texas Surgical Society. The American College of Surgeons did me the honor of electing me a fellow. I have had the honor also of serving, at one time or another, as president of the county medical society; twice as president of the Texas Surgical Society, and as a vice president of the Texas State Medical Association. I also joined various civic and political groups. In fact, I joined just about everything except the Republican party.

Call me a joiner if you want to, but I can say, without crowing from the housetops, that these associations and connections have brought me a certain satisfaction beyond the wildest dreams of the Mississippi farm lad who hunted for bones around the railway company hospital. Perhaps my boyhood environment and my days as a country doctor have made me crave fellowship.

I revel in the affinity of the three great professions—education, law, medicine. Sometimes it is hard to draw a line between them. Joined together in one great cavalcade, the teachers and lawyers and doctors of the world could be a powerful force for good. I'm not a one-worlder, either.

In spite of the ups and downs in my own political fortunes, I believe a doctor should take an active interest in public affairs. I think he should participate in politics from the local precinct to the White House. I don't mean partisan politics; I don't think he should run for office.

I have practiced what I preach. I have never run for office or applied for a political appointment. The only time my name ever appeared on a ballot was in 1940 when I was a presidential elector from my congressional district. I have held commissions under five different governors, but these appointments were tendered, not asked for.

I have been a delegate to every county and state Democratic convention for fifty years; a delegate alternate to the national Democratic convention in 1940, and a member of the Texas State Democratic Executive Committee in 1948–50.

I know that the local precinct, the smallest political subdivision, is the place to get started on the things that a doctor would like to see done. Our political principles, policies and platforms go back, in one form or another, to the local precincts.

I have in mind such things as the establishment of the first sanatorium in Texas, the veterans hospital, and the organization of a state board of medical examiners and a state health department.

By this time you have decided that I must be a Democrat. I am. No apology, no prefix, no suffix, just a Democrat. But I have a wholesome respect for old-time Republicans and I believe in the two-party system.

I have named some educators who had influence on my career. In many ways the progress of education during the first half of this century paralleled the advancement in medicine. We've come a long way from the one-room, one-teacher school. I look forward to the day when every pupil will have available not only a nurse, dentist and doctor, but also a trained psychologist and, if need be, a psychiatrist.

Many lawyers are politicians and lawmakers. I daresay the majority of the members of Congress and of the state legislatures are learned in the law. They also should know something about medicine and public health.

Right now the crying need in Texas and in many other states is for something to be done about our mentally ill. We treat insane people as if they were criminals. They are not criminals, they are sick. One of the first things we need to do in Texas is abolish the mandatory trial by jury of insane persons. A proposed constitutional amendment may remedy this situation.

The very idea that an insane person should have to be tried by a jury of his peers—a competent jury, they call it—

is ridiculous and repulsive. Too often this is a haphazard procedure. Too often the jury consists of loafers picked up around the courthouse. Who knows that they are competent? Who knows that they are sane themselves?

Texas, I believe, is the only state in the Union, at this writing, that still insists upon the mandatory jury trial. Many states adopted the plan when in the mid-nineteenth century there were exposés where sane individuals were railroaded to institutions and deprived of their property through the machinations of others who had selfish motives. But a scientific system of determining insanity can be established along with safeguards against abuse.

This is primarily a medical problem, not something to be left to the sheriff, the constable, the county judge, the justice of the peace, and the courthouse habitués. Individuals should not be "accused" or "charged" with insanity, as if they were criminals.

While Texas is the lone offender with regard to the mandatory jury system, other states, too, might find room for improvement in handling their unfortunates. The importance of this problem generally is obvious in statistics of the U. S. Public Health Service. According to these figures, 50 per cent of the hospital beds in the United States are devoted to mental patients. About 97 per cent of these patients are maintained in hospitals operated by government agencies financed by American taxpayers.

If teachers, lawmakers and doctors can't do something about this situation, I don't know who can.

While I am on the subject of mental hygiene, I would also mention the difficulty of adequate provision for sterilization of insane persons. A Texas lawmaker asked my comment on a bill which he was about to offer.

This fellow's bill would have authorized boards of state institutions to examine mental patients with a view to sterilizing those "who would produce children with an inherent tendency to feeble-mindedness, insanity, epilepsy, criminality or degeneracy, and there is no probability that the person so examined will improve to such an extent as to render procreation by any such person advisable, or if the physical or mental condition of any such person will be substantially improved thereby."

The proposal went on to say that it was not intended as a punitive measure (very generous, indeed), but for the betterment of the patient and for the protection of society.

The board's decision to sterilize could be appealed to the courts by the patient, by his next of kin, or by his custodian.

The bill, intended to apply to both male and female insane, proposed also that sterilization should be carried out on persons convicted three times or more of a felony and sentenced to serve in a penitentiary.

The measure provided that the surgeon performing the operation should not be held liable, criminally or civilly, for any loss or damage except in cases of negligence in the performance of such operations.

To which I replied, "While the bill may provide that a doctor cannot be sued, there are no provisions which prevent him from being killed."

I had in mind the young lunatic who came to my office with that ugly six-shooter after I had made him sterile.

"So personally, if the bill should be enacted," my letter continued, "I would not care to be the official sterilizer.

"My observation is that most of the people who are running around talking eugenics are themselves standing astraddle the boundary line between sanity and insanity; and if the bill should be passed I suggest it include such persons, and professional politicians, quack doctors, shyster lawyers, libertines, etc. That would just about put the proposition on a basis to benefit the coming generation."

The lawmaker replied he would amend the bill to include members of the House as fit subjects for sterilization.

But, more seriously, my letter had gone on:

"This bill has many good features. However, I fear it would prove to be a very unpopular and unenforceable law. It is not definitely established that feeble-mindedness, insanity, epilepsy, criminal tendencies, degeneracy and sexual perversion are all hereditary diseases or conditions. Many of them are, but there would be a constitutional question should we undertake to draw a discriminating line. Personally, I am in favor of the bill, and I would give it a much wider range. I certainly would include drug addicts and habitual drunkards. Perhaps there are more people outside institutions who should be sterilized than there are found within. I see no good reason to have insane persons sterilized until such time as they may be discharged. It is not definitely established that sterilization would improve either the physical, mental or psychic condition of an inmate. It is reasonable to conclude that inmates of these institutions would have very little chance of procreation. Furthermore, the manner of determining just which one of these inmates, insane persons, or criminals should be sterilized might be attacked as to its constitutionality. The Bill of Rights proclaims that a person shall not be deprived of life, liberty or property without due process of law. And rarely does a man get so crazy or mean that he does not consider his so-called manhood a valuable property right, a prerequisite of his liberty and something almost as dear as life itself."

Well, my letter and an amendment to the bill proposing that legislators, too, be sterilized were enough to defeat the measure.

It all boiled down to two facts: No one wanted to be the official sterilizer and no one wanted to be deprived of the pursuit of happiness.

At any rate, these wrangles stirred interest in a topic that is likely to be with us for a long time to come. And, indirectly at least, the discussion has turned to a finer objective—curative measures for the insane through the use of new drugs and chemicals. This is a field where much remains to be done.

Modern facilities for the rapid dissemination of news and for the exchange of views speed up the processes of expression, argumentation, rejection and selection. And in that alchemy the residue is progress.

There is no yesterday in this profession. What was theory yesterday may be accepted as fact today and discarded as a fallacy tomorrow.

Sometimes, even with the free and easy flow of information, progress seems slow, and we may find ourselves right back where we started. Take the medical treatment of appendicitis, for instance.

The vermiform appendix is what doctors call "an anatomical vestige," or a leftover, in the body. There is a theory that in the dim and distant past, when man's food was coarse, this hanger-on to the stomach, which today varies in length up to nine inches, performed a function. For many thousands of years man has had little or no use for the appendix, and in today's mashed-potatoes-and-gravy age he has less use for this anatomical vestige than ever.

However, this useless gadget can cause trouble because it is very defective in structure, in drainage and in blood supply. Both moralists and evolutionists might say that the fate of all things that fall into disuse is deterioration and death. So far, the appendix, puny as it is, has managed to hang on. At least, almost all human beings are born with it.

Maybe it is a good thing it has survived. It gives people a chance to talk about their operations. Otherwise, they would be listening to the radio or looking at television, and the social grace of conversation would die for lack of exercise.

The ancient Egyptians and Babylonians studied appendicitis and other diseases, and kept careful records as to symptoms and remedies. There were some laws that required any person cured of a disease to report his findings to the priests in the temple. The idea was to spread the knowledge of remedial measures. This principle we follow today in spite of international political rivalry.

But what I was going to say was that among the ancients there was a gadabout and scribbler by the name of Strabo. Strabo was a good reporter. He came across the case history of Rhamos, the grain merchant. Here is Rhamos' story as reported by Strabo:

"I am Rhamos, the grain merchant, and I live on my boat on the Nile. I have always observed the teachings of the Hiero Biblos, have kept to my regimen, and have not eaten of forbidden fruit nor drank of the unsavory waters of the river. I have purged myself on three successive days, once a month. But of a sudden I was stricken with a hard pain in my bowels. I spewed out my food and drink and had a painful swelling in my belly. I was overcome by a raging fever. I was carried to the temple and lain on a slab and a cold poultice of herbs placed on my belly. The food and drink brought me was consumed by the serpents of the temple and for six days I famished. I was then fed on goat's milk and gradually my strength came back."

Apparently this fellow Rhamos had an attack of acute appendicitis. If so, he received the very best of treatment.

According to one school of thought, this treatment, dating back 2,000 years before Christ, basically should be followed today. Four thousand years have not altered the nature of appendicitis, have not varied the clinical symptoms and have not changed very materially the medical treatment, short of operation.

Consider again the treatment Rhamos got and compare it with the treatment many doctors prescribe for appendicitis today:

1. Put the patient to bed.
2. Place an ice pack or cold application to his abdomen, over the site of the appendix.
3. Withhold all food and drink from him, absolutely everything, not a bite of food, not a drop of water.
4. Cool his fever with an icecap to the head and keep him quiet. If the diagnosis has been settled, give him narcotics to relieve his pain.
5. Supply fluids by proctoclysis (rectum), normal saline, or bicarbonate of soda, 2 per cent in ordinary tap water.
6. When the fever symptoms have subsided, cautiously begin to give liquid nourishment by mouth.

And don't purge. Remember the old saying, "Purgation spells perforation." Fight shy of enemas.

I have performed appendectomies on persons ranging from a six-hour-old baby girl to a ninety-two-year-old lady. Both operations were successful.

Even though some of our methods of treatment fundamentally are no different from what they were centuries ago, we have made tremendous strides in other directions. It has been only about a century since Ignaz Semmelweiss was run out of Vienna because he contended, "Puerperal fever (childbed fever) is caused by the conveyance to the pregnant woman of putrid particles derived from living organisms through the agency of the examining fingers." He argued that obstetricians were sowing the seeds of death at childbirth. The same thing had been happening the world over, of course, and it was many years after his pronouncement before the situation was corrected.

I have recalled how as late as 1901 a learned medical society in New York was debating the question whether a surgeon should use rubber gloves or his bare hands. Today there is no longer any doubt in anyone's mind. Up to this good hour no absolutely foolproof way to sterilize human hands has been found. While the surface may be scrubbed more or less effectively, there remains the sub-surface, with its microscopic crevices, where deadly germs may lurk. The use of rubber gloves offers the greatest factor of safety, and even then caution should be exercised lest tiny punctures in the gloves release lethal organisms into the patient's system.

More recent advances that should be mentioned are international collaboration in combating influenza, tuberculosis, malaria and venereal disease, and in the establishment and expansion of public-health services in many countries.

There is the relatively new field of chemotherapy. Some of these miracle drugs can be overdone. We can make the same mistakes we made at the turn of the century in stoking our malarial patients with quinine. But because we overdo a good thing does not rule it out entirely.

All in all, the discovery of penicillin and the development of antibiotics generally have made great contributions to medical science. Some of these things have come about through vision, design and struggle, others through luck.

The late Sir Alexander Fleming, discoverer of penicillin, made the statement that his discovery in 1928 was "pure luck." It took us almost fifteen years to capitalize on this stroke of good fortune. It wasn't until World War II that mass production of penicillin started, and it was not until after the war that it became available for the civilian population.

It is good to remember this whenever we are inclined to become impatient with the efficacy of new vaccines and other innovations.

In one of his last public statements before his death in 1955, Sir Alexander predicted that all microbes would be brought under control by the year 2000.

"Twenty-five years ago," he was quoted as saying, "very few microbes could be dealt with in the human body, and there are still a few that dodge us. But they will be beaten before the year A. D. 2000."

That is a wonderful prospect. I shall not challenge the prediction even if I have some mental reservations.

The reason I would not gainsay it is because I have seen too many changes within my own span.

I have had something to do with two great natural disasters. I sketched the relief mission to the Galveston hurricane area in September, 1900. The other one was a tornado that struck Waco, a city of almost 100,000 population, on May 11, 1953. It killed 114 persons, injured more than 500 and resulted in some $50,000,000 damages in an area of two square miles in the heart of the city.

In this north-central Texas city we were not used to tornadoes, or twisters, as these furies sometimes are called. Such disturbances occur every now and then in the South and Southwest. But Waco is just a little bit out of what has come to be known as Tornado Alley. The favorite trail of the "dancing devils," as the Indians used to call them, is across northern Louisiana, northern Texas, southern Oklahoma and southern Arkansas.

During the last few years the weather bureau has set up a tornado-warning system, something like the hurricane-warning service, which has been operative for some years. A hurricane meanders around for days and days and there is a chance to chart its probable course to some extent. A twister makes up in a few hours, strikes with the suddenness of a serpent, then recoils as if horrified by its own havoc, and then perhaps hits elsewhere with equal fury. There was a warning for the Waco area, but, human nature being what it is, most people went on about their business. There wasn't much they could do anyway; no meteorologist could pinpoint the area where the tornado was likely to strike.

It hit at 4:45 p. m. with heavy rain, hail and a wind that reached an estimated velocity of 100 miles per hour. Within less than one minute buildings up to five stories tall, in the neighborhood of the towering Amicable Building, crashed like houses of cards or exploded like toy balloons. Wind and atmospheric pressure wrecked several blocks.

Within minutes the fire and police departments and the

city's hospitals and doctors were on the job. Within an hour after the storm struck the Army, the Air Force and the National Guard had the situation well under control, and the removal of the injured, the dying and the dead proceeded in an orderly manner. It is true that there were one or two cases where the injured were not found under the debris until some hours later, but generally the rescue job was finished within a few hours. There was little looting.

After the Waco disaster I could not but compare notes, in my own mind, with what had happened on previous occasions. In the Galveston hurricane I am sure that many persons trapped under debris died many hours later without hope of rescue. Rescue was rare, and relief was slow in reaching the island, and the facilities for taking care of the injured were limited. In Waco the hospitals very easily absorbed all those who needed hospital care. Modern drugs and technique saved many lives. I recall that in the gin-boiler explosion at Holland my own home had been converted into a small hospital.

And I remember World War I when our boys died because we had no vaccine against gas gangrene.

So, when I hear people talk about "the good old days," I wonder just what they mean.

I'll take today. I am thankful, for example, that I have lived to see the development of a vaccine against infantile paralysis, although there have been temporary setbacks in its use. After all, progress does not make a beeline.

Through my associations and from my own experience I formulated my golden rules of surgery, which are:

1. I will not advise a surgical operation on any of my patients unless I would be willing to have the same opera-

tion done on myself or on a member of my family under the same conditions and circumstances.

2. I will not undertake any kind of surgical procedure on any patient unless I am convinced I can do as well or better than anyone else within reach of my patient.

Adherence to these rules will prevent many useless and unnecessary operations and also many prolonged and inadequate procedures. Those are two of the greatest sins in surgery. Unnecessary or prolonged surgery due to lack of skill, training and experience is both thievery and potential legalized murder. These are harsh words, but I know of no other adequate way to express it.

Closely connected with unnecessary and unskilled and inadequate surgery is this business of fee splitting. This is a vicious, unethical practice whereby the family doctor, or internist, or specialist who first has the patient in charge, has a secret arrangement, or "gentlemen's agreement," with the surgeon or specialist to whom the case is referred. Then the two parties participating in the transaction split the fee, usually fifty-fifty. This is without the knowledge or consent of the patient or of the person paying the bill. The result is higher fees and often unnecessary, frequently dangerous, surgery because better surgeons do not fall for such unethical practice.

So I have a word of advice for the laity. One of our leading jewelers has a slogan which I hear in commercials over the radio. It is, "If you don't know diamonds, know your jeweler." And I would say, "If you don't know what's wrong with you, know your doctor; and if you need surgery, know your surgeon."

THE GOLDEN AGE

I HAVE five grandchildren. They used to follow me about the hospital from floor to floor and sometimes from room to room. One day some ladies cornered me and asked, "Doctor, tell us how to grow old gracefully like you so we can enjoy our grandchildren."

I was in a hurry so I gave them a quick answer:

"Keep your feet warm, your bowels open and your conscience clear."

That recipe frequently was quoted at the clubs and the sewing circles, much to the embarrassment of my family. Still it's a good formula as far as it goes.

There are all kinds of recipes for longevity, of course. Not long ago a ninety-year-old patient of mine came in for a checkup, and I asked him how he managed to outlive his wife for so many years.

He said, "Well, when we married seventy years ago we made an agreement that when I got mad at her she would shut herself up in the kitchen and when she got mad at me I would go outdoors. I stayed outside most of the time, got plenty of fresh air, and outlived her by twenty years."

Some of the old-line life insurance companies have made a compilation of the longevity of married folks. They came up with an interesting report. The average life span of married women is seven years more than that of the married man. The average man was five years older than his wife when they married. That adds up to the conclusion that the average married woman can look forward to twelve years of virtuous and happy widowhood—the Kinsey report to the contrary, notwithstanding.

I know that if in my time interviewers or snoopers had gone around talking to our womenfolk about their private lives they would have been shot or tarred and feathered and run out of the county. Where I grew up some things were inviolate and unquestioned. These were a man's veracity and integrity, a woman's virtue, the established boundary lines and the branding marks.

It may be that some of our aberrations are due to the feeling that civilization apparently had reached a sort of dead end during World War II. The possibilities of the nuclear age had not shown up in their finest form.

It has not been so long ago that many young persons began to feel that there were no new frontiers to conquer. Frustration and defeatism were in the air. The advent of the atomic age did a lot to dispel the gloom. Scientific advances have opened up entirely new fields. Virgin frontiers beckon on this planet and in interstellar space. The sky is no longer the limit.

What miracles nuclear developments will bring to medical science remain to be seen. There is no doubt that better tools for diagnosis already have been brought forth. Much other research remains in the field of trial and error and controversy. A great deal of rubbish will have to be cleared away before the real nuggets are found.

Longer, more useful human life is an attainable goal.

Already we have increased longevity to a point where we are having trouble coping with the problems that arise in connection with a growing percentage of an aged population.

Older folks, caught in the jam of a changing economic and social world, are asking, "What shall we do?"

Long ago I quit advising my elderly patients to retire. I don't like the word "retire." It means to recede, retreat, withdraw, back up, stagnate and then make an early demise.

I am inclined to believe that the policy of many government agencies and other corporations to retire employes in their sixties is an economic and political fallacy. I am convinced that such a policy is a physiological and psychological error. Many persons reach intellectual fruition between the ages of sixty and ninety.

In my own case, I consider my most fruitful years from age sixty-eight to seventy-eight. At sixty-eight they turned me down for military medical service in World War II.

Since medicine has become so highly specialized there is a slowly developing specialty known as geriatrics. That is the science and art of the management and treatment of elderly people. Medical science has increased the average life-expectancy. So there are more and more older folks. Consequently, there is ample room for geriatrics in every city and community. There is more than science in the treatment of elderly people; it takes a lot of art, patience and understanding to keep them "tolerably well" and happy.

I don't know what all these problems are, but here is the way I feel about it:

That "old age" of which we speak is that happy, peaceful and fruitful estate which marks the declining years of an honorable, useful and earnest life. Old age, to be honorable and worthy of emulation, must rest upon a foundation laid by youth, builded by young manhood and maintained by middle age.

Cicero, in his apostrophe to Scipio the Younger, said, "Neither white hair nor wrinkles can at once claim influence in themselves; it is the honorable conduct of youth and early manhood that is rewarded by possessing influence at the last."

Certainly we must all know that the course of life is fixed. We recognize that nature permits the race of life to be run but one way and only one time on this earth. To each part of life there is something especially seasonable. The helplessness of babyhood, the feebleness of childhood, the wavering and hesitancy of adolescence, the wild and exuberant spirit of youth, the soberness of middle age and the ripe wisdom of old age—all these have a certain natural advantage which should be secured by all in the proper season.

We can have these advantages but once; that is, the pleasures and pains, the joys and sorrows and the benefits and disappointments of each phase of life come but once to each individual. Yet there is a cumulative result. Each period of life, or we might say each day of life, adds to the preceding one until the sum total finds expression in the mental, moral, spiritual and physical attributes of old age.

The attainment of old age merely from the standpoint of years is a worthless achievement. But the victory of adjustment and poise over the perplexity of youth and the indecision of middle age is a reward toward which the normal mind should incline naturally.

Come to think of it, there is no good reason why the young should hate to grow old, knowing that naught but an untimely death will prevent old age. And there is no good reason why the old should hate to be old, seeing that the few who have reached that goal are favored.

Of course, there comes a time when older people will slow up, but that does not mean they are through. After all, life is made up largely of unfinished business. One never gets so old that he does not think of something he would like to do. For instance, if I had the money and the time I would cross the ocean again, journey to the Lake District of England and worship in the Crosthwaite Church, founded by my forefathers 1400 years ago. That is an ambition. Why shouldn't old folks have ambitions? We have got into the bad habit of speaking of "youthful ambitions" as if they were a monopoly of youth, as if ambition were inseparable from youth and forbidden to old age. It is said, "Youth must be served." Why? Isn't there enough to go around?

The time is coming when the irreversible forces of nature will compel me to lay aside the scalpel and suture material. I shall have to take my last stitch. Almost eighty-three years of age, my hand is perfectly steady, my mind is clear, and I can act and think as I could when I was in my forties and fifties. But I tire easily when I stand on my feet in prolonged surgery.

Obviously when I reach the point where I feel I cannot do as well by my patients as anyone else available, it will be time to leave them in younger hands. I shall not relax my interest in my chosen profession. It has been the prop on my leaning side that has kept me straight, upright and happy.

I consider myself a success in my chosen profession; I think of myself as a failure, financially.

Now, since I claim success in my profession, you ask me what I have to pass on in the way of medical and surgical knowledge.

Nothing. There is nothing I can say to the oncoming generation of fine young doctors who, after long years of study and training, are ready and anxious to take over. They are of another era, on the brink of the atomic age. Medical and surgical procedures will be revolutionized, maybe not overnight, but gradually.

Medical science and the practice of medicine and surgery have made steady progress even from the days of Hippocrates and Aesculapius. They and their students and followers rescued the science from the confusion and impotency of empiricism. Through the thousand years of intellectual night the devotees of medicine, often serving as both priests and physicians, carried the torch which lighted the way out of ignorance and the murky miasma of human misery. The Renaissance, with its great upsurge in culture, science, art, music and invention, failed to free the benighted mind of humanity from superstition and prejudice relating to the treatment of disease.

For a long time medicine seemed to lag behind. We read of great epidemics such as smallpox, yellow fever, typhoid, typhus and bubonic plague destroying entire cities and countries while the doctors who suggested new methods of prevention and treatment were persecuted and sometimes banished. Infection decimated armies and turned military hospitals into morgues.

The enlightened public today may inquire why the doctors did not rise up against these conditions. That is a story that probably never will be told. It is beclouded by too much individualism. Of course, in later years, a few names stand out such as Lister, Pasteur, Semmelweis, Koch and some of our own immortals like Osler, Cushing, Wyeth and others.

It was about the close of the last century when medical organizations began to function, after we had cast off some of our individualism. Cooperative and group practice came into useful activity. Clinics were formed in many of the centers of population. Medical colleges were being reorganized and reclassified, and medical teaching was being standardized. Medicine and surgery branched out into various specialties.

I believe that every specialist ought to have several years of general practice. I have advocated legislation in Texas similar to that of some other states under which loans or grants are set up for medical students with the proviso that they practice for several years in some small town or rural community where a doctor is needed.

My advice to a young doctor is to find a good country town where they need a doctor, and start a general practice. There are hundreds of such communities in Texas and in other states. I can think of one offhand: Holland, Texas. They used to have a half dozen doctors in Holland; as of this writing they don't have one.

The things that loom large on the horizon may be mirages. I remember my boyhood dreams of New York, Philadelphia and Chicago. The little things in little towns sway the course of empire and of men. Call it coincidence or luck or your guardian angel, but it is there.

To the surgeon I would say: Don't be ashamed to pray.

You need a silent partner, some invisible one to stand by your elbow and guide your hand and mind through the operation. Prayer will give strength, courage, assurance and confidence. It will steady your hand; it will clear the cobwebs of indecision from your brain.

Then, I would add: Don't get impatient, especially about money matters. The practice of medicine and surgery is primarily a profession, not a business. Some doctors get rich, usually from wise investments and consistent saving. Others die poor, usually because of bad business ventures or extravagant and wasteful habits. Whatever your lot in life may be, my advice is to follow the old Indian rule to "take what you have and do the best you can with it."

To grow old gracefully is an art. Live each day as if you expected it to be your last day on earth.

No one likes to be reminded that he has a bright future behind him, but the doctor who ministers to generations in a community will become an object of devotion and veneration.

The venerable New Orleans surgeon, Dr. Rudolph Matas, had this in mind when, in his nineties, he told newsmen after many honors had been bestowed upon him, "I grow a bit tired of these funeral orations."

The old doctor will be feted on anniversaries. He will be showered with presents such as ties, socks and sports shirts unsuited to his style of dress, and he will be praised for the good work he has done.

But all this devotion and praise will bring him little comfort. His pleasures will be filled with regrets. When he is reminded by Mrs. Chance that he saved her life, he will be thinking of little Mary, who died of gangrenous appendicitis and how, with modern methods and antibiotics, little Mary could have been saved.

Or he will think of someone near and dear to him who could not be saved with all that science could offer.

I am thinking now of Mrs. Doctor, who died August 17, 1955, eight days after a stroke.

I have made the statement that I consider myself a financial failure. I'm not much of a bookkeeper—and most doctors are notoriously poor businessmen—but I suppose I have made a million dollars in my time. I don't know where it all went. Some of it was lost in hard times; a lot of it was spent in trying to keep abreast of what was going on in the world of medicine and surgery.

At any rate, my graduation-day band again can strike up that old refrain: "Oh, Mr. Johnson, turn me loose; I have got no money, but a good excuse."

I am going to offer some excuses now, not for myself but for the guidance of those who may have a more practical turn of mind. If I had been a better manager I might have been a multimillionaire. I don't believe that old poppycock that opportunity knocks at your door but once and that if you don't open the door, opportunity moves on, never to return. For me, at least, opportunity has knocked again and again.

It just seems to be predestined—in the cards, so to speak—that some of us remain poor and others get so lousy rich they can't sleep well.

They say it is an ill wind that blows no good. There is something to that.

When we got through with the three-weeks relief mission after the Galveston storm in 1900 we moved on up to

Houston, to the old Auditorium Building. While we were crossing over on the ferry a man fell down a ladder of the ferry. He was a Captain Hardin, a passenger. I took care of him, he recovered from his fractures, and we came to be good friends.

He owned three sections of land at Sour Lake, Texas. He wanted to sell that land and he kept after me to buy it. His indebtedness on it amounted to about $1,000. He would turn the property over to me if I would just assume the indebtedness. Other than Mr. Hearst's roll I had no money.

There was a two-story building on the property, and a well. Captain Hardin told me about that well, and how the Indians used to come around there and drink that Sour Lake water for medicinal purposes. He urged me to take the 1,920 acres and put up a sanitarium there—one of those water-cure spas, you know. He also had a pipe stuck in the ground from which he was getting his fuel. Natural gas—and plenty of it—he kept telling me. No one thought of oil there then.

Anyway, I had no yen to acquire property in that part of the state, especially after that hurricane had rolled through there.

I bought Captain Hardin a ticket to Virginia. Last thing he said was that he would send me a note and the deed on the property, and he did. I stuck the papers in a pigeonhole of my desk. They were still there when the first oil-producing well was brought in on that property. Not until then did I think about putting the deed on record, and by that time some of the lease brokers had beat me to it. Just the lease money on that property ran from $1,000 to $2,000 per acre.

That was destiny.

If I had taken that property I would have been a millionaire, I might have quit practicing, and the world might have been better off! Who knows?

Thereafter I got a bit oil-minded. I was called up to Muskogee, Oklahoma, to testify in federal court about an arson case. During court recess another witness and I took a walk around the countryside. We saw an apple orchard, the fruit red ripe. I wanted to buy an apple, and we went over and talked to the old-timer who owned the orchard. He said he had ten acres there. I noticed he had natural gas burning from a pipe to heat the kettle of water while his wife was washing. I asked him whether he wanted to sell. He said yes; his wife was ailing and they wanted to go back up North. He wanted $1,000 for the ten acres.

I told him I would take it. I asked a lawyer to look over the abstract and I went back to Texas. That lawyer turned out to be mistaken, and he wrote me that the title to the ten acres was no good. It wasn't long until there was a cluster of oil wells in and around that apple orchard.

That was another time that opportunity knocked, but it just didn't pan out.

My point is that opportunity does knock again and again. Don't let the commencement speaker tell you otherwise.

I have never seen many doctors—who I thought were real doctors—who were also good business managers. Their minds just don't run that way. They don't seem to grasp business opportunities and make the most of them.

Maybe the Lord arranged it that way. Just think what the world would be like if He had made all doctors a grasping, avaricious lot. There would be combines, mergers and monopolies by individuals and groups who, in many cases, would hold the power of life and death. The cash register might overshadow the stethoscope.

Within my lifetime an entirely new branch of medical science has been popularized. That is psychiatry, dealing with mental diseases and disorders, their causes, symptoms and treatments. For centuries there had been some research, but it wasn't until Viennese, German and Swiss doctors such as Sigmund Freud and C. G. Jung came out with such things as psychoanalysis in the late nineteenth century that popular interest was aroused.

Then, in the 1920s there came to our shores a French pharmacist, Emile Coué, with his hypnotic treatment called autosuggestion. His recipe was simple: Just keep repeating, "Every day in every way I'm getting better and better." It was said that adherence to that psychology would cure anything from insanity to ingrown toenails. A foxtrot, "I'm Getting Better and Better Every Day," was a popular dance tune of the time. Someone asked Coué whether antosuggestion would cure typhoid fever and he said he didn't know, he had never tried it.

I've never tried it either, so I don't know whether it would work or not. The Lord knows I would have tried autosuggestion many years ago had I had faith in it. Brother Bob died of typhoid, Dr. Border's fever gave us many anxious hours and through the years I lost patients to typhoid.

I do know that Coué and his abracadabra did not hurt my business. Folks kept getting sick. The pharmaceutical houses and the drugstores did not fold up.

I am persuaded, though, that there is a certain therapeutic value in mental recreation. Texas is rich in folklore and for half a century I have been running into the legend of Rattlesnake Sam and his friend Pete. Sam was a super-frontiersman, perhaps a kinsman of Paul Bunyan of the north woods and John Henry of Negro folklore. Pete, a rattlesnake of gigantic proportions such as could grow only in Texas, was his constant companion. Their exploits have been told and retold for generations. I have seen patients, especially psychosomatics, forget all about their ills in telling the story of Rattlesnake Sam and his friend Pete.

I remember the first time I heard it as if it were only yesterday. It must have been back in 1898. A woman in northeast Texas wrote me a letter "to come see my old man."

It was a long ride to the weather-beaten clapboard house on the bluff overlooking the river. He must have seen me coming. At least, my approach by horseback sent a flock of buzzards wheeling into the sky. The vultures had been fussing over a long carcass at the foot of the bluff. To me it looked like the remains of a huge snake. My patient was standing at the gate, rubbing his right thumb against his right forefinger.

"Get down, Doc," he greeted me.

First I thought he was rolling a cigarette with one hand, as waddies were wont to do, but as I dismounted I noticed it was an empty gesture—a mannerism, I thought. There was no cigarette.

"Many snakes around here?" I inquired.

"Nope, few little un's, but ain't seen a real big rattler around here for quite a spell," he said. "Thirty years ago there was a heap o' snakes, and some tough hombres, too. Did you ever hear 'bout Rattlesnake Sam and his friend Pete?"

"Can't say that I have."

He eyed me appraisingly while the nervous rubbing of thumb and forefinger continued.

"Well, nigh thirty years ago we had one o' the driest o' the dry years," he began, while the nervous gesture gradually came to a halt. "Hadn't rained in a month o' Sundays. Lost some o' my best cows on Boggy Branch. Red River she dried up, too, and it was easy crossin' to Oklahomy. One hot afternoon during the dog days me and the neighbors was at the store at Three Forks, just a-sittin', a-chawin' and a-whittlin'. All at once we saw the biggest cloud o' dust this side o' tarnation. Mind you there weren't a breath o' air a-stirrin', but it looked like a cyclone a-comin'. We all run fur the storm house dug behind the store. That cloud o' dust shot right up to the hitchin' rack in front o' the store and when it settled a big son of a gun jumped from his seat in a two-wheeled cart. Hitched to the cart were two man-eatin' panthers, frothin' at the mouth and hungry-lookin'.

"Everybody started gettin' further back in the storm house."

I began to wonder what mental storms my patient had undergone. First I was convinced that his was a case of delirium tremens, but I had to abandon that theory when he showed concentration and coherence in the story of Rattlesnake Sam. Furthermore, I observed, during his narrative his cigarette-rolling mannerism was arrested entirely.

My patient, apparently calmer than ever, went on to recount the saga of this fabulous character and his friend, the snake.

"Where did he come from?" I asked innocently.

"Well, Doc, one o' the fellers in the storm house asked that question, too, an' the last thing we heard the stranger say as he pulled out was, 'I'm Rattlesnake Sam and this is my friend Pete, and they run us out o' Oklahomy because they said we wuz sissies.' "

My patient cackled over the rather corny ending to his part of the legend. Since then I have heard the story again and again, in various versions. Through the years the exploits of Sam became more and more daring; his rattler friend, Pete, grew to gargantuan size, and this strange pair of man and beast just about had their own way in their dealings with all mankind and the snake kingdom.

But what interested me there, and thereafter, was that the narrator usually became so absorbed in the telling of the yarn that he forgot all about his ailment.

There was nothing I could do for the cowman who first told me the legend. He had Parkinson's disease, commonly called shaking palsy. He would go on until the end of his days—and I understand he lived to a ripe old age—rubbing his thumb and forefinger. But I felt repaid for the long ride by the hope that perhaps the treatment of some nervous disorders lay in the fields of psychology and psychiatry.

It isn't such a long jump from the Sam-and-Pete legend to the Davy Crockett craze of 1955. This ballad and all the trimmings that went with it seemed to give a natural escape and antidote to the parlous times in which we lived —a sort of psychological antibiotic.

I'm not suggesting that these recurrent crazes can keep us from going crazy. In fact, sometimes I think we are becoming "curiouser and curiouser."

The point is that I had a whole lot rather deal with a

patient who can relive the exploits of Rattlesnake Sam and Davy Crockett than with one who imagines he is Napoleon Bonaparte.

I had rather have a patient who finds peace of mind in folklore than one who is obsessed with the menace of Halley's comet, Martian invasions, flying saucers and, to be more realistic, of destruction in a nuclear holocaust. There is mental hygiene in legend and other folklore, but we have to know when and where to apply this therapy.

I am well aware of the fact that in repeating this folklore and in speculating on its therapeutic value I am groping in what to us today is darkness.

It is worth thinking about. Along with nuclear developments and the probe into outer space, we are on the frontier in the exploration of the human mind.

I am glad to be living in this age. I feel that during my fifty-six years of practice probably more verities in medicine and surgery have come out of the crucible of time and trial than during any other comparable period in history. And the best is yet to come.

EPILOGUE

As I have grown older I have been asked frequently about my views on religion and immortality.

My first rule of life is this: Stay on good terms with yourself. If you are true to yourself it follows naturally that you will not, in fact you cannot, be false to your family, your community, your country and, above all, your God.

Dr. Taylor, the grand old man of medicine in Holland, was one whose philosophy of life had a great influence on me. Many times, when I was struggling to get a start, he gave me sage advice.

One day he said to me, "I am tired out, just worn out, so I am going home to bed and stay there until I die, and that won't be very long."

It wasn't.

He had two maiden daughters who cared for him during his last days. Many of his old-time friends and patients came to see him. One old lady especially appeared to be greatly worried about him. One day she prolonged her visit, and the doctor asked her if there was something she wanted to say to him.

"Yes, Doctor, there is," she said. "You are getting weaker

and won't be here much longer. I want to know if you have made your peace with the Lord."

"No."

The old lady was horrified. She pleaded, "Doctor, please make your peace with the Lord."

He said, "Look here, lady, me and the Lord have never had a falling out. I don't have to make my peace with Him; I have always been on good terms with Him."

And the doctor died gracefully.

From the beginning of humanity there never has been a race so primitive that they did not believe that in some manner there was an existence beyond the grave. There never has been a civilization so exalted that it did not adhere to the belief and hope of life everlasting. From time immemorial the prophets, priests, preachers and philosophers have extolled the glories of life after our time on this earth has ended.

It is true that there are now, and always have been, individuals who deny the existence of a Divine Being, or boast of their doubt as to the authenticity of the Bible. I have known individuals like this. I have been with some of them in their last moments, and I have never seen one die holding on to such beliefs unless it was a case of sudden death.

No one can live happily, or die peacefully, without an abiding hope of immortality.

When I have laid aside my stethoscope and my last day on earth is ended I am confident that a new day will dawn; a new life will come, a new existence springing out of my earthly sojourn.

It seems ironical and contrary to all the laws of nature that a person should cease to exist just because he stops breathing into his lungs the life-giving oxygen which is so abundant all around him.

As I have stood by the bedside of many who have passed on, I have felt the last flicker of the feeble and failing pulse. I have felt the last flutter of the weakening heart. I have seen the light fade slowly from the eyes.

Now I am going to tell you something that for many years has held me captive in a fog of speculative thought.

When the family and close friends gather around a loved one who is dying they are entirely too disturbed emotionally to be able to observe a phenomenon such as I shall attempt to describe.

One rainy day I was called to the bedside of an elderly lay preacher. He was dying with double pneumonia. I placed my stethoscope over his heart, my fingers on his feeble and fading pulse. His eyes were sunken and lusterless. I felt his last pulse beat; I heard the last flicker of his tired heart. I was looking straight into his eyes.

With his last breath there came a flash of light from his eyes such as I had never seen before and such as I have seen only once since then. He seemed to strain forward from his pillow to get a better view. In a fraction of the bat of an eye a peaceful smile came over his shrunken face. It was so spectacular that I looked up toward the ceiling in an effort to see what he saw. I saw nothing extraordinary.

I have heard the expression "out of this world." The light of the eyes in that fleeting instant was something literally out of this world.

I am sure that the good old man was permitted a glimpse of the beauties and glories of life beyond the grave.